*The restless land*

# The Story of Tongariro National Park

Tongariro National Park

# INTRODUCTION

Hard by the windswept plain a small outpost of beech and scrub intrudes a finger of dark green into the black of the night. Within the beech a morepork calls. Stars, clearer than they can ever be in the city, form a pattern of pinpricks of light in the sky. Slowly the bulk of the Kaimanawa Ranges begins to outline the east, and as the light spreads, the first rays of dawn turn the snow-clad peaks a soft pink. The plain is suddenly dominated by the mountains, majestic in their solitude, spreading north and south, revealing the scars of volcanic fires long past. Morning has come to the Tongariro National Park.

The day will bring with it a new sense of wonder for all those who pass by, for you cannot travel through the Islands of Maui, this strange fish-shaped land, without this Park touching your very existence. For those who visit the Park, it means different things. For some, the swish of skis on newly fallen snow. For others the heart stopping challenge of rock and mountain climbing; where every fingerhold is as important as the next breath; the still beauty of the rimu forest, with the spreading canopy of green sheltering a wonderland of life as it once was; the weary exhilaration of the tramper, following a path between tussock and lava flow; or the fascination of the volcanoes, where the steam on hillside and mountain top tell tales of the awesome power of the very lifeblood of the earth itself.

The unique role of this Park, first in a series of National Parks throughout New Zealand, wreathed in tribal lore, and an area of ultimate contrasts of fire and snow, forest and tussock, volcano and glacier, cannot be described in words. It must be savoured; experienced piece by piece. And as it reveals itself it becomes compulsive, for each new discovery leads inevitably to a quest for the next.

Importantly, the Park is sacrosanct, a piece of New Zealand which society has decreed shall remain as near as possible unaffected by Man's developing instincts. The Tongariro National Park administration has been entrusted with the responsibility of maintaining the Park, and striking the right balance between our use of the Park and the need to allow it to change at its own pace. This handbook has been commissioned by the Parks administration to help give a basic understanding of the Park and its environment.

# CONTENTS

# MYTHS AND THE MOUNTAINS

The mountains of the Tongariro National Park stand aloof from the Central Plateau, contributing to and modifying the appearance and climate of the surrounding landscape, majestic in their mystique. It has always been so from man's first acquaintance with the Tongariro mountains. For the Maori they were the **matua,** or parent of the land, the centre of his **mana,** he identified with them as his **tupuna** or god-like ancestors; when the Pakeha arrived he too viewed them with awe and appreciation, and invested them with an aura of beauty and magnificence.

The origin of the mountains of Tongariro are entrenched in Maori mythology.

In the long ago (so James Cowan quotes the tribal saga) there was an assemblage of great mountains in this heart of the Island—there were more than you see now. Like gods they stood there. Tongariro was chief of them all, but in the far away days lofty snow-topped Taranaki stood there too—he stood where the round lakes Nga Puna a Tamatea lie now—and there also stood here Tauhara, and Putauaki, (now called by the Pakeha, Edgecumbe). They were males, all these mountains; they were gods and warriors—all except one who was a female. Her name was Pihanga. Yonder she stands still, the crater-dented, gently rounded eastern buttress of the Kakaramea Range. Her richly coloured robe of forest is held closely about her. Of a surety she is a female, as you may see from her shape.

And all these mountains loved Pihanga and each wished her to become his wife. But the one she favoured most was Tongariro—we regard Ngauruhoe and Tongariro as one. He won her by fierce combat; he turned upon the other mountains and he forced them to depart. He fought them and defeated them. Pihanga was his.

And the defeated mountains debated among themselves whither they should go. They said to each other "We must separate, we shall go this way and that, for Pihanga belongs to Tongariro." And Tauhara and Putauaki, who stood where Roto-a-Ira Lake is now, said to the other mountain, "Yes, we shall go hence; we shall go to the sea which looks towards the rising of the sun." They would go to the sunny north and east, to the Bay of Plenty where there was room for mountains. And Taranaki said, "I shall go to the setting place of the sun." And so they parted, those mountains, they uprooted themselves and they travelled far away, crying their farewells to Pihanga, who was now the wife of Tongariro.

"Remain you here, O Pihanga," they said, "we are going away."

The mountains travelled all through one night. It was a magic pilgrimage, in the hours of darkness, the only time when fairies and mountains can move abroad. Taranaki travelled west; he travelled fast and angily and at daylight he halted at the sea coast; and he is called Mount Egmont now. Tauhara and Putauaki travelled north, towards the morning sunshine.

Putauaki was halted by the dawn-coming when he had travelled the greater part of the way to the sea, and there he stands to this day at the northern end of the Kaingaroa Plain, nearly 160 kilometres from his original standing place, looking down on the wide valley of the Rangitaiki. He is the Ngati-Awa's sacred mountain; a great cone of green and blue, with a capped summit; the dead crater holding a little lake.

But Tauhara was the slowest of the rejected lovers. He travelled with tardy lingering steps; he paused many times to look back towards Pihanga, whom he was leaving. And when daylight came and stopped his march he had only reached the place where he stands yonder, near the shores of Taupo Moana. And he ever looks back across the lake at beautiful Pihanga.

So there the mountains stood, and it was many centuries before they came alive with fire. The legends tell that Ngatoro-i-rangi, the great priest, in his wanderings reached the Tongariro mountains. He climbed Ngauruhoe to spy out the land, but when he had ascended to the summit he became enveloped in a sudden snowstorm, a new and terrible experience. In his extremity he cried out to his priestess sisters back in the northern land:

"E Kuiwai e! Haungaroa e! Ka riro au; te tonga! Haria mai he ahi moku! (O Kuiwai! O Haungaroa! I am borne away in the cold south wind—I perish from the cold! Send me fire to warm me!)

His sisters heard him, and they persuaded the fire-demons to send volcanic fire by way of White Island and Rotorua, bursting out of the ground in many places before reaching the peak-top, saving Ngatoro-i-rangi with its warmth. Ngatoro slew a female slave named Auruhoe to give his prayer more strength; when the life-giving fire burst forth Ngatoro threw her body into the burning crater thus giving the volcano its name. The words 'riro' (seized) and 'tonga' (south wind) in the prayer of Ngatoro-i-rangi were the origin of the name Tongariro.

These legends and other like them are the Maori explanation, steeped in tradition and mystery, for the presence and activity of the mountains of the Tongariro National Park. Alongside them runs the account of their origins taught us by the evidence of the rocks of the volcanoes, a story no less vivid and intricate in its unfolding, for it is a story of fire and rivers of mud, of mountain-building and cataclysm, a story that is written on a page of New Zealand's history that is two million years and more old and has not yet reached its conclusion.

# THE GIFT

The story of man's involvement with the mountain, plains and life of the Tongariro National Park is just as fascinating as the story of its creation by volcanic forces. Although the record of human influence on the Park is only fleeting compared to the geological record, man's influence in shaping the Park is second only to the influence of the volcanoes.

From the time that the Maori's eyes first fell on these sentinels of the Great Volcanic Plateau, he had a respect bordering on awe and reverence for the mountains, drawing from them the basis of mythology and legend. Although the legends of the Great Migration are now lent little credence by anthropologists, they remain important in Maori history, and the mountains have a direct link with the arrival of the first canoes.

One of the great canoes was named Te Arawa, with the great ariki Ngatoro-i-rangi as high priest, and Tamatekapua in command. After landing at Maketu, Ngatoro-i-rangi surveyed inland to claim domain for his tribe, travelling around Lake Taupo to Tokaanu and Rangipo. Meeting a challenger for the land, Ngatoro called on his gods, who sent dense black clouds and snow down to the desert and his rival, with his party, perished from the cold. Since then the desert has been known as Rangipo (darkened skies), and Te Onetapu (the sacred sands) have been held so sacred that the Maoris travelling through it used to wear leaves to keep their eyes on the track. Ngatoro continued to the top of Ngauruhoe, where, as we have seen, he called forth fire to keep himself warm.

Eight generations later in a line of direct descent from Ngatoro-i-rangi was the great warrior Tuwharetoa, whose name was taken by the whole tribe at a later time; this was the mighty Ngati Tuwharetoa tribe, who claimed the mountains because of Ngatoro's claim, and defeated the Ngati Hotu and Ngati Ruakopiri to confirm the tribe's domination.

Later the Ngati Tuwharetoa elected a paramount chief of all the sub-tribes to maintain unity. The first such chief was Herea, who later adopted the family name of Te Heuheu. Herea was a wise chief, living in the fortified Waitahanui Pa near Turangi.

Herea's son, Mananui Te Heuheu, was the next Paramount Chief, and became the most distinguished chief in New Zealand. He was over two metres tall and was renowned for his wisdom. His

This Park, the nucleus of which was gifted to the people of New Zealand in 1887, is a memorial to Chief Te Heuheu Tukino and the Tuwharetoa people.

name and tribe were linked to the mountains by the Taupo Maori saying "Ko Tongariro te Maunga; Ko Taupo te Moana; Ko Tuwharetoa te Iwi; Ko Te Heuheu te Tangata." (Tongariro is the mountain, Taupo is the great sea, Tuwharetoa is the tribe, Te Heuheu is the man.)

In 1840, when Mananui was Paramount Chief, he was approached by the new European Government to sign the Treaty of Waitangi. In a spirit of independence that was a forerunner of later King Country resistance to European domination, Mananui refused to sign.

Mananui had shifted the location of the main tribal village to Te Rapa, near the present village of Waihi. In May 1846 rainfall caused a great landslide which enveloped the village, and entombed most of the inhabitants, including Mananui and his eldest son.

His brother, Iwikau, took over the chieftanship, and in 1856 he presided over a conference of many tribes which decided that Tongariro should be the centre of a district in which no land should be sold to the Government. At the same time, Iwikau told the assembled chiefs he believed they should abide by the Treaty of Waitangi.

When Iwikau died in October 1862, Mananui's younger son Patatai, known as Horonuku ("Landslide") in memory of his father, became chief—Te Heuheu Tukino IV. A chief of great standing, his loyalty to the Maori people brought him into conflict with the Crown. On one occasion he led more than 200 warriors to help the Waikato tribes in their fight against the Europeans. And he was involved in Te Kooti's battles with the Government forces at nearby Te Porere.

But Horonuku was chief during a time of great transition, and his achievements resulted in the preservation of the Tongariro area from annexation either by other tribes or by the now familiar Pakehas. Indeed, one of his sons-in-law was Lawrence M. Grace, M.P., son of the pioneer missionary, Rev. T. S. Grace.

In the 1880's Keepa Te Rangihiwinui Taitoko (Major Kemp) claimed part of the area. Aware that Europeans were beginning to covet the tussock lands for sheep farms, he appeared in the Native Land Court at Taupo, and spoke of his ruapatu rights, the fruits of conquest. He had, he said, kindled his fires in the land, his ahi ka had burned in South Taupo. He claimed, therefore, a voice in the allotment and disposal of the land.

Te Heuheu heard the speech with rising anger. He rose and answered. "Who are you", he said, "that speak of your fires of

12

occupation burning in my country? Where is your fire, your ahi ka? Where is it? You cannot show me, for it does not exist. Now I shall show you mine! Look yonder." The proud old chief pointed across the great lake, southward to where a coil of yellow vapour rose from Ngauruhoe's crater. "Behold my ahi ka, my mountain Tongariro. There burns my fire, kindled by my ancestor Ngatoro-i-rangi. It was he who lit that fire and it has burned there ever since! That is my fire of occupation! Now show me yours!".

The wit and force of the argument silenced Keepa Te Rangihiwinui Taitoko, and he found it useless to press the claim any further.

But, although he had saved his lands from claims from other tribes, Te Heuheu foresaw another problem. The European Government was progressively defining the Maori land, dividing it up into legally described parcels. How could he be sure that once this was done the sacred mountain lands might not be sold off to the pakeha? As long as he was alive the mountains were safe, but future generations were an unknown quantity.

He discussed the problem with Lawrence Grace, his son-in-law, who suggested a solution, "Why not make them a tapu place of the Crown, a sacred place under the mana of the Queen. The only possible way to preserve them for ever is to give them to the Government as a reserve and park, to be the property of all the people of New Zealand, in memory of Te Heuheu and his tribe."

The Chief agreed, and a meeting between Te Heuheu and the Native Minister, the Hon. John Ballance, was held at Rotorua. Assured that the Government would accept the gift, Te Heuheu in September 1887 formally offered his land as a National Park, an offer which was accepted by the Government.

The Tongariro National Park was established in 1894 but not gazetted until 1907. It consisted of the original gift block of 6,518 acres with another 56,000 acres purchased later. Today it has expanded into a park of 188,000 acres (75,500 hectares). Tongariro National Park was one of the first National Parks in the world, the first being Yellowstone National Park in the United States of America.

Horonuku died in 1888, and was succeeded by his son Te Heuheu Tukino V, Tureiti. Upon Tureiti's death in 1921, his son Hoani became Chief, and he in turn was succeeded by Hepi (created Sir Hepi Te Heuheu in 1978), the seventh Te Heuheu Tukino, Paramount Chief of the Ngati Tuwharetoa.

Early Pakeha interest in the Park area lay in two directions—an understandable interest in the mountains themselves on the one hand, and an interest in exploiting the surrounding countryside on the other.

The first attempt at sheep farming in the Taupo district came as early as 1856, when a small flock was brought into the area from Hawkes Bay at the suggestion of the missionary, Reverend T. S. Grace. They were kept at Pukawa, north west of Turangi. The Maoris living around Lake Rotoaira were impressed by this new venture, and together raised £187 for their own flock. The Rev. Grace brought 170 sheep for them with this money, and later in 1857 another £136 was raised and further sheep bought.

However, the wars and general unrest between Maori and Pakeha in the surrounding areas in the early 1860's led to the abandonment of this initial sheep farming venture in the Park area.

In 1875 E. Moorehouse brought sheep onto the blocks south east of Ruapehu as did a number of Maori owners. In 1879 J. and L. Grace, backed by T. Norrin, stocked the Okahukura Block and in 1880 Walker and Smith leased the Te Henga run. Grace Brothers first brought in a flock of 4,000 sheep, in 1879 another 2,500 and in 1880 3,000 more.

But this venture, too, ran into difficulties. There were no fences, so stock losses, especially from wild dogs, were a real problem. The area was very isolated, and shipping out of wool was difficult. One method was to pack by horseback the 100lb bales to Lake Taupo, where the wool would commence its long trip to Auckland by boat up the Lake. Another way was to trek the wool to Napier on the Kuripoponga Track, and a third involved sending the wool on horseback to Pipiriki, and then down the Wanganui River.

These problems, coupled with the fact that the sheep didn't altogether like eating the tussock, led to the decline of sheep in the area in the early 1900's, and by the 1920's sheepfarming no longer existed.

The first white explorer to climb any of the mountains was a Mr J. C. Bidwill, who ascended Ngauruhoe on March 2nd and 3rd 1839, and the second explorer of the mountain was Mr Dyson, who visited Ngauruhoe in March 1851. As far as can be gathered from these early explorers' accounts the crater was much deeper than it is now, and it did not contain the two subsidiary craters.

The Tongariro mountains have always held a special fascination for climbers. This party visited the crater of Mt. Ngauruhoe shortly after the turn of the century.

Many of the early explorers of the mountains had difficulty in persuading the local tribes that their activities were not going to upset local customs. Sir George Grey found this a problem—in 1850 he came to the area to attempt a climb of Mt Ruapehu, but thought it wise to accede to the demands of the local Maoris and give up the idea, for the time being anyway.

In January 1853, with the Rev. Richard Taylor, he ascended the Ringatoto Spur, probably to the summit of that peak. His claim to have made a later ascent to the summit of Ruapehu cannot be substantiated. It was not until March 1879 that George Beetham and J. P. Maxwell became the first Europeans to reach Ruapehu Peak and see the Crater Lake.

The first hut near the Park was a wooden slab hut built in 1880 by Rawiri Ketu as a shepherd's cottage for the Tongariro Run. Wi Takarei, a young shepherd was found dead there in 1882, after which the hut was burnt to the ground. The local Maoris regarded the place as being haunted by the ghost of a young woman who had been murdered there, and believed that the ghost had something to do with the shepherd's death.

John Grace built another hut (known as the Haunted Whare) about a quarter of a mile away, and it is said that the ghost of a handsome young Maori woman visited the hut frequently. The site of the Haunted Whare can be seen on the left of State Highway 48 to Whakapapa, just above the Tawhai Falls Track.

Tourists to the Park had an adventurous journey in these early days. A typical expedition would be from Wellington, catching a coastal steamer to Wanganui, and travelling up the Wanganui by river boat. The river boats had to winch themselves through the rapids, and would then reach Pipiriki, where the tourists would have to disembark to stay at the hotel at the township.

From Pipiriki, they travelled by stage coach to Raetihi, from Raetihi to Waiouru, and then along the desert Road Track to the Waihohonu Hut. This hut, which still stands as an Historic Building, was built of corrugated iron with a double wall and a 200 mm thick pumice insulation layer. Another coaching hut was built around the same time near the Ketetahi Springs.

Two major influences in the area around the Park in those early days were the building of the Main Trunk Railway and the extensive timber milling around Ohakune and Erua. It was the completion of the Main Trunk Railway in 1909 that switched the

The historic Waihohonu Hut still stands on the western flank of Mt Ruapehu. Rough roads and transport didn't deter early visitors to the Park.

emphasis from the eastern side of the mountain to the western side bringing with it the development of the Whakapapa Village.

In the large forests that covered the land south and west of Mt Ruapehu, logging for timber became a major industry. In the early 1900's over 20 mills were operating in the Ohakune, Raetihi and Rangataua district. The timber that was produced from these mills was used to persuade the Government of the time to route the Main Trunk railroad around the western side of the Park. However shortly after this, as much of the forest had been cut out, the mills gradually began to close.

The last section of the line to be completed was through the rugged territory around Mt Ruapehu. The construction workers in these rough and ready times lived in tent camps, and stories of slygroggers operating in the Park area during the prohibition days abound.

A feature of the building of the line was the major engineering problems that had to be overcome. One difficulty was bridging the deep stream gullies that flowed down from Mt Ruapehu. Viaducts were built, using prefabricated steel sections pulled to the site by bullock teams. The only exception was the huge Makatote Viaduct between National Park and Ohakune, where steel was cut to plan in the Anderson workshop and erected on the site.

The Raurimu spiral was another achievement, still regarded as the only way to bring the railway line through the area and up to the Volcanic Plateau.

On the 6th November 1908, two trains met, signalling the completion of the main trunk railway. An obelisk marks this point at Pokaka, just south of National Park. At the same time, roads were being used by motorised transport and in 1912 the first car completed the journey from Wellington to Auckland, passing up the western side of Mt Ruapehu on the very rough clay track.

It was the opening up of the area by the railways and the road that enabled people to come to the Park in far larger numbers than was possible with the stage coaches. Increasing numbers of visitors put pressure on the accommodation facilities and the very few huts in the Park area. The first huts for tourists at Whakapapa began to be built in the 1920's and additional huts, dining halls and recreation rooms were added as visitor numbers began to increase. In August 1928 the Tongariro National Park Board negotiated an agreement with the Tongariro Park Tourist Company Limited to construct a hotel at Whakapapa.

The foundation stone for what was to be the Chateau Tongariro was laid on the 16th February 1929 and some 120 men were engaged on the project. The hotel was built for the sum of £78,000, most of which was loaned to the company by the Park Board, and the hotel opened for business on 1st August 1929.

In two years however the Tourist Company struck financial problems and went into liquidation in 1931. The hotel passed back into the Park Board hands as mortgagees and the Board operated the Hotel for one year until the Tourist Department took over the management of the hotel. At this time the first Ranger in the area,

Mr Alf Cowling, was instructed "that his services were to be at the disposal of the Manager of the Chateau and that his horse was to be available when not otherwise required for hiring out to guests." Rates in 1931 for staying in the hotel were 22/6d per day with ski hire at 3/6d a day or 17/6d a week. The chef earned a wage of £17.10s per week.

The Chateau has had quite a career. After many years as a hotel, in 1942 it was used to house patients from the Porirua Mental Hospital, following the Wellington earthquake which had destroyed the hospital in Porirua. In 1945 all patients and staff were evacuated because of the large eruption of Mt Ruapehu. The hotel re-opened in 1948, and in 1976 was extensively refurbished.

With the availability of more extensive accommodation facilities, the Whakapapa area became even more popular and in 1938 the Tourist Department installed the first rope tow on the mountain, of about 450 feet. The tow was installed from a point about a quarter of a mile above the old Salt Hut to near the present site of the Tauwira Ski Club lodge.

From the Maori legends through to the present day the park has had a long and involved history. A history of conquest and war, of legends passed down and an area that has had a special place for as long as man has enjoyed living in New Zealand. Its present status is a tribute to the foresight of chief Te Heuheu Tukino.

Opposite page:

Skiing started by W. P. Mead in 1913 gradually built up in popularity over the years as the ski fields and access roads improved. Here a group (1938) pictured outside the old Salt Hut prepare for a day's skiing.

For over 50 years the Chateau Tongariro has provided a focus for accommodation and hospitality.

19

## THE RESTLESS LAND

To man, in his three score years and ten on this planet, nothing is more immoveable than the earth on which he stands. Yet the geologists now know that the world is a dynamic one, composed of an interlocking series of rigid plates rafted on a fluid core. The plates are in relative motion at rates of a few millimetres per year and where plates collide great forces are generated. At some plate boundaries one plate bends and slides under its neighbour. The buckling and friction associated with the plate motion generates heat and causes melting at the plate junction. The molten rock, or magma, generated rises through fractures in the upper plate and a chain of volcanoes forms on the surface near the collision zone between the plates.

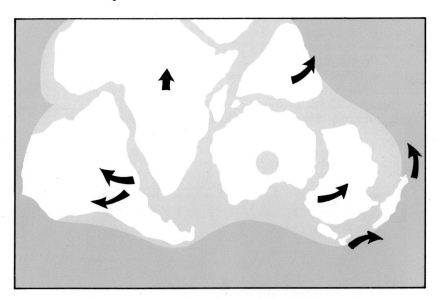

## Moving land masses

The earth's crust is composed of major rigid virtually undistorted slabs or plates. These plates have been moving for hundreds of millions of years, and are still moving. Once New Zealand was part of a large continent comprising Australia, Antarctica, India, South America and Africa. NZ drifted apart less than 100 million years ago, but association with these large continents can be seen in some of our plant and animal life.

A plate boundary lies just east of the North Island of New Zealand, where the Pacific Plate is overridden by the Indian-Australian Plate, and the line of volcanoes from Tonga to Ruapehu is the result. The buried Pacific Plate lies at a depth of 150 km below this zone of volcanism. Geologists divide the zone into three regions: a central region (Rotorua-Taupo) dominated by the products of rhyolitic eruptions, and regions of andesitic volcanism to the north (White Island-Edgecumbe), and south (Kakaramea-Ohakune). Rhyolite and andesite are types of volcanic rock defined by their chemical composition; the former rich in silicon and very thick, the latter rich in calcium, iron and magnesium and relatively fluid. The southern region is known as the Tongariro Volcanic Centre and it contains four major andesitic volcanoes, Kakaramea, Pihanga, Tongariro, and Ruapehu.

The volcanic mountains which dominate the park are very recent features. Many millions of years ago, when the New Zealand land mass was in the process of formation this area formed part of the sea floor. A layer of marine sedimentary rocks known as greywacke lies beneath the modern volcanoes, formed by compaction of the ancient sand and silt beds of the sea floor. The same greywacke units form the rugged Kaimanawa Ranges to the east of the park. The greywacke land mass rose above sea level for

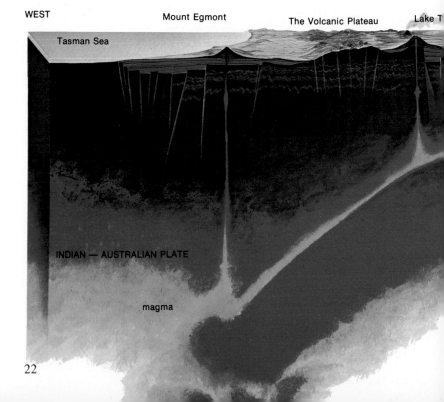

WEST               Mount Egmont       The Volcanic Plateau     Lake T

Tasman Sea

INDIAN — AUSTRALIAN PLATE

magma

some time, but 30–40 million years ago it sank again and a further sequence of sedimentary rocks accumulated over the basement of greywacke. These softer and younger sediments can be seen as upstanding blocks below Hauhangatahi and as cliffs of light coloured mudstone and siltstone behind the Ranger Station at Ohakune. Mollusc fossils and the remains of other marine organisms are found embedded in some of the rock layers.

The history of volcanism in Tongariro National Park is very short indeed. Geologists estimate from the presence of andesitic pebbles in sediments of the Wanganui district that volcanism started 2 million years ago (compare this with an age of 5000 million years for the earth as a whole, or 200 million years for the greywacke of Kaimanawa). However the exact source of this very early volcanism is not known. Geologists estimate the age of volcanic rocks using the known rate of decay of radioactive chemical elements, particularly potassium and uranium. The oldest rock from the park dated by this technique is a 261,000 year old lava flow from Mt Tongariro.

nawa Range    Hikurangi Trench    EAST

Pacific Ocean

PACIFIC PLATE

## The restless land

The planet Earth comprises a very hot, dense, iron-rich inner core enveloped in a thick mantle of near liquid rock. Earth's crust is solid rock, just a few kilometres thick, floating on the mantle. The crust is thinnest across deep ocean basins, and thicker beneath the landmasses.

Modern geophysical research has shown that the crust is divided into regions of independent caps, called plates. These plates move by converging, parting, or sliding past each other, carrying the landmasses with them.

Along a line from near Raoul Island, as far south as central North Island, relatively thin oceanic crust of the Pacific Plate buckles down beneath the Indo-Australian Plate. In this process, known as subduction, the rigid plate initially cracks as it buckles, but as it heats up by deep immersion in the mantle it softens and becomes pliable. It eventually melts. Heat from this system escapes upwards to melt part of the continental crust. This, with small amounts of melted oceanic crust, forms *Andesite* magma which finds its way up cracks to form volcanoes like Egmont, Tongariro, Ruapehu and Ngauruhoe.

# The landscape today

This active volcanic landscape shows many phases of volcanic activity. The older volcanoes of Mt Ruapehu and Tongariro are more eroded and scarred. Ngauruhoe, still growing, has the cone formation that Tongariro once had.

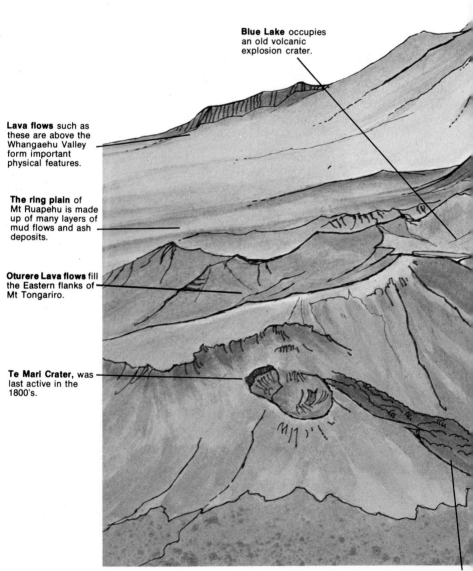

**Mt. Ruapehu** 2797m, this mountain is made up of several vents, lava flows, ash deposits and mud flows.

**Blue Lake** occupies an old volcanic explosion crater.

**Lava flows** such as these are above the Whangaehu Valley form important physical features.

**The ring plain** of Mt Ruapehu is made up of many layers of mud flows and ash deposits.

**Oturere Lava flows** fill the Eastern flanks of Mt Tongariro.

**Te Mari Crater,** was last active in the 1800's.

The **Te Mari** lava flows.

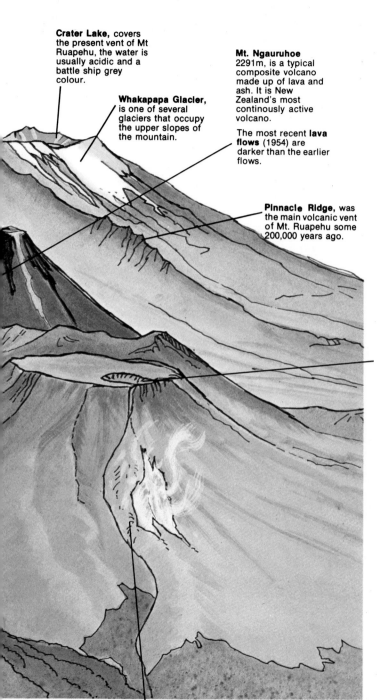

**Crater Lake,** covers the present vent of Mt Ruapehu, the water is usually acidic and a battle ship grey colour.

**Whakapapa Glacier,** is one of several glaciers that occupy the upper slopes of the mountain.

**Mt. Ngauruhoe** 2291m, is a typical composite volcano made up of lava and ash. It is New Zealand's most continuously active volcano.

The most recent **lava flows** (1954) are darker than the earlier flows.

**Pinnacle Ridge,** was the main volcanic vent of Mt. Ruapehu some 200,000 years ago.

**Mt Tongariro's** flat topped truncated cone is the result of a massive eruption.

**Ketetahi springs,** is an area of thermal activity.

Volcanic activity can be intermittent, continuous, or occur just once. Volcanoes that erupt intermittently may erupt maybe once every two, three or four thousand years or at longer intervals up to half a million years apart. Examples of these types of volcanic eruptions are found in the Taupo area, for example Lake Taupo, and the Lake Rotorua area. These volcanic vents have erupted spasmodically over the last two million years and the last eruption from Lake Taupo was about two thousand years ago.

Some areas of volcanic activity are continuous and a good example of continuous volcanic activity is the Wairakei area. The physical landscape can indicate the type of eruption that has occurred. Where the eruptions are moderate, debris piles up and will build up a cone like Ngauruhoe or Mt Egmont. Where the activity is violent, debris is dispersed widely, as in the case of the Lake Taupo eruptions.

The expansive waters of Lake Taupo have had an explosive past. Beyond, are the active volcanoes of Tongariro, the ending point of the Pacific ring of fire.

Various striking physical features of the Park are the result of volcanic activity. The attractive conical shape of Mt Ngauruhoe is a result of two thousand years of minor ash and lava eruptions building up a near perfect cone. Mt Ruapehu is an example of a volcano that has been made up of several vents, many lava flows and many different mud flows over thousands of years. The lava flows that have occurred from the different vents during the last few thousand years now are seen as large rock bluffs and outcrops. The lower slopes of Mt Ruapehu which surround the complex mountain are made up of mud flows and debris which has erupted out of the vents.

The Park's northern boundaries extend as far as the two extinct volcanoes of Kakaramea and Pihanga. State Highway 47 runs between them as it crosses from Turangi to Tongariro. Both are less than 1 million years old, and both were extinct while Tongariro was still active.

Mount Tongariro itself was formed by a large number of volcanic vents which over a period of time from 2 million years ago deposited successive layers of lava and volcanic ash. It's believed that once Tongariro was cone shaped, not unlike Mt Ngauruhoe is today. At one stage the upper section of the mountain collapsed as a result of a violent explosion.

The older vents of Tongariro ran in a line stretching from the West crater to the Oturere Valley and almost to the Tama Lakes. When the mountain collapsed, about nine new craters were formed, including the present South, West, Central, Oturere craters and Pukekaikiore.

About 20,000 years ago a new burst of activity from a series of vents modified the shape of the mountain greatly. These vents were particularly active in a line between Te Mari and Ngauruhoe, and eruptions at the same time were responsible for the building of Pukeonake.

### YESTERDAY'S LANDSCAPE

This is how the landscape may have appeared at the end of the last Ice Age 20,000 years ago. Glaciers filled the higher valleys. Volcanic activity may have been quite continuous, these eruptive phases would have been dramatic with the hot explosive material, lava and steam mixing with snow and ice to form mud flows.

27

More recent activity has built Mt Ngauruhoe, and formed Red Crater, the explosion craters where the Emerald Lakes now lie, and Te Mari. At Red Crater an ash eruption was recorded in 1855, although the volcanic activity in the area is now reduced to steam and gas vents at the northern end.

Upper Te Mari crater was formed as recently as 1869, and erupted most recently in 1896 when ash up to 50 mm thick fell on the Desert Road and reached as far as Napier. Near this crater, lava flows less than 1800 years old have spilled down the hillside into the Okahukura Bush.

On the northern slopes of Mt Tongariro the Ketetahi hot springs with their fumeroles and boiling mud pools are a vivid reminder that the mountain is still far from extinct. The springs are believed to have been more active in the past, and in the 1890's mud erupted from the area and was washed down into Lake Rotoaira.

The volcanic plateau from above Turangi, looking over Pihanga towards Tongariro, Ngauruhoe, Ruapehu.

A riven, blasted landscape pitted by craters, Red Crater, still active, and the Emerald Lakes which fill old explosion craters.

The most spectacular recent eruption was the formation of Ngauruhoe. Really part of the Tongariro vents, Ngauruhoe because of its prominence and activity is usually regarded as a separate mountain. Activity began about 2,500 years ago, with most of the almost perfect cone being built of layers of lava and airborne debris within a short time. The 30° slopes reach up 900 m from the base to a height of 2291 m above sea level, where a 400 m diameter crater contains both the original craters and a 60 m high cone on the western side formed by eruptions in 1954. During this eruption lava spouted more than 300 m in the air and Ngauruhoe effortlessly tossed out boulders 15 m across. An estimated 5 million cubic metres of lava streamed down the western face leaving behind a rugged pile of scoria up to 20 m thick.

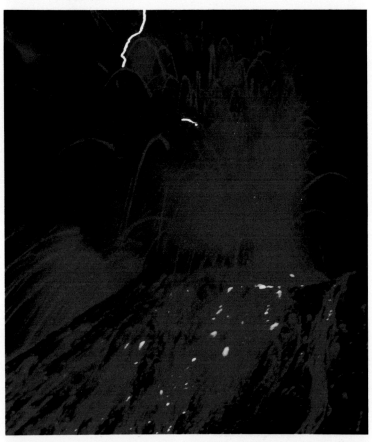

Mt Ngauruhoe effortlessly tosses boulders hundreds of metres into the air during the 1954 eruption. The 1975 eruptions were dominated by ash and steam clouds which rose thousands of metres.

The Mangatepopo Valley is bounded on the left by glacial moraines from the last ice age and on the right by the old eroded vent of Pukekaikiore. Young Ngauruhoe dominates the skyline.

Below left:
The Active Crater of Mt Ngauruhoe

This recent activity of Ngauruhoe underlines the fact that all the volcanoes are still very much alive. Over the years ash eruptions reaching high into the air, sometimes as high as 9 km, avalanches of steam, hot gases, boulders and debris, lava flows, and expelled scoria blocks have all been recorded, with the most recent spectacular activity of this kind happening in 1975 at both Ngauruhoe and Ruapehu.

Long before Ngauruhoe was formed, to the south of Tongariro arose Mount Ruapehu with its older lava flows dating 1 million to 250,000 years ago. Like the other mountains of the region it was formed from successive layers of erupted lava, and ash. At 2797 m, Ruapehu is the highest point in the North Island, and was probably never much higher than this. The mountain looks as if it was once higher and the top has been knocked off, but this is due to the large number of collapsed of craters along the 3 km length of the mountain—East Crater, the two craters of North Crater,

Beneath Mt Ruapehu's seemingly placid Crater Lake lies a lava plug. Sometimes, its activity results in eruptions of steam and mud. Mud flows called lahars, like this one, have over thousands of years built the surrounding countryside. In 1969 and 1974 they have damaged some facilities on the ski field.

Girdlestone Crater, and West Crater including Crater Lake. Hauhangatahi, 12 km to the north-west, was associated with this initial development of Ruapehu.

Relatively recently, lava flows have come from a small parasitic cone 1500 m above sea level on the northern slopes of the mountain, and further eruptions have occurred at Ohakune.

The main crater of Mt Ruapehu has changed its location several times and is now in its most southerly position; once it was near Pinnacle Ridge. Nowadays, the crater is usually filled by a lake, except in periods of moderate volcanic activity. Often, when Ruapehu erupts, water from Crater Lake is expelled and causes

When the lahars reach the plains they can pile up into large mounds like these several kilometres below the Chateau.

mud flows (lahars). These have been occurring for thousands of years and are responsible for the characteristic rounded hummocks found at the junction of State Highway 47 and 48. The rush of water from the Crater Lake due to the collapse of ice at the Crater Lake Outlet was responsible for the 1953 Tangiwai rail bridge disaster.

This then is the nature of the geology of the Park, a saga of fire and eruption, devastation and rebuilding, a story that is yet to be finished but one which has already left a landscape of such importance that its unique place in New Zealand's heritage was formally recognised more than a century ago.

About 80 million years ago New Zealand separated from the ancient southern Continent that scientists have called Gondwanaland. From that time our vegetation has developed in relative isolation, although it shares a common ancestry with the present vegetation of Australia, India and South America and with the fossil vegetation of the Antarctic.

The great span of time involved in the processes of plant ecology makes it difficult for us to comprehend the fact that the life cycles of plant communities are often more complex than our own.

The relative isolation in which our vegetation has developed, makes the study of its cycles comparatively easy. When European settlement of New Zealand began in the mid eighteenth century the study of botany was quite advanced. In New Zealand the early botanists discovered a vegetation which was highly developed and largely unmodified. The botanists of Europe had studied a vegetation which was, by comparison, much harder to understand, as its development reflected centuries of interference by man.

New Zealand's vegetation provided a unique insight into the story behind the development of plant communities that were not

subject to the influence of man. These opportunities are steadily diminishing throughout modern New Zealand, and our National Parks and Ecological Reserves are rapidly becoming ecological islands in a sea of change.

The vegetation cannot be considered in isolation from the fauna. The idea of ecology is that all things relate, that the story of the forests is the story of the birds, of the insects, of the land animals. The idea of ecology shows that everything affects everything else, that we cannot make changes in the forests without causing far reaching effects on other forms of life,

Although many of our plants have a common ancestry with plants elsewhere, many others have developed and changed over millions of years to become unique. New Zealand has a significant number of plants which are not found anywhere else in the world, these are called endemic. Likewise, our insect and animal life reflects this isolation. Some insects and animals surviving in New Zealand are no longer found anywhere else in the world.

To understand the development of New Zealand's flora and fauna we must understand the forces which have moulded them.

In the southwest, Ruapehu rises 2,000 metres above the plains. Here there is a great variety of ecological habitats, with much beauty and interest.

41

The most obvious influence is that of climate—the climate we have today has itself been subject to radical changes in the past.

The world has gone through dramatic changes in average temperatures. Colder periods have brought major ice ages, with the last significant cold period starting about 2 million years ago and ending about 15,000 years ago.

The cold temperatures, with their resulting ice and snow produced a large number of glaciers and also caused the sea level to drop far below the present level.

The conditions then favoured an expansion of the alpine plants and depressed the rain forests and sub-tropical plant communities.

Because of the increase in suitable habitat the diversity of alpine plants increased significantly. The low sea level meant that there was no ocean barrier between what are now the three main islands of New Zealand, and it was possible for the alpine plants to migrate throughout the landmass.

As the climate gradually warmed the glaciers retreated, the sea-level rose and the land bridge between the islands was cut. The conditions now favoured the expansion of the rain forests and the sub-tropical forests, which caused the alpine plant zones to diminish.

There is no reason for us to imagine that these processes of change have ceased. The climate and vegetation that we have today is not stable, it is only a point along a line of continual change.

The plants and animals of New Zealand have endured many such changes over the millions of years of their development. Man is a relative newcomer, whose influence over the natural course of events seems puny by comparison.

The delicate beauty of the gentian and other alpine plants contrasts with the severe environment. Snow can cover the park at any time of the year. Alpine plants like this tussock adapt to the wide ranges of climatic conditions.

43

## Plant communities

To understand the fundamentals of plant ecology we need to begin by considering the individual plant, its life and its requirements. We must then look at the plant in its community and see how some of its requirements are met by other plants around it. The life of plant communities is as fascinating as the life of their individual members.

What is a plant? It can be comething as simple as the single celled algae of the Emerald Lakes. Or it can be as complex as the mighty rimu.

Whatever form they take, individual plants all have common needs and features. Most obviously they require food. Green plants take in carbon dioxide from the air and combine it chemically with water to produce nutrients called carbohydrates. This food manufacturing process is known as photosynthesis and it can only be carried on in the presence of sunlight. As well as carbon dioxide, plants need certain minerals from the soil which they use to make proteins.

The essential requirements for any plant are access to nutrients and to sunlight. Individual species of plants have adaptations which enable them to survive in the incredible range of conditions which exist. Stand in rain forest and look up at the tallest trees. Their leaves fill almost all the available space as they compete with each other to reach the sun. Plants which cannot reach these levels have adapted to survive on the filtered sunlight beneath the forest canopy. The broadleaved plants, ferns and fungi are all examples of plants which survive in the damp, warm climate of the forest understory.

The plants must also reproduce. Methods of reproduction range from the simple splitting of single celled plants through to the complex sexual reproduction of flowering plants. This reproduction of flowering plants produces seeds, which are a major influence on the food chain of birds, animals and insects. It is also a process

A rich profusion of life, each plant relying and competing with its neighbour for existence. Seeds from plants in the Park are distributed in different ways. The seeds of the Bidibid—*Acaena microphylla* attach themselves to animals. The seed of the brightly coloured snow buttercup—*Ranunculus nivicola* are dispersed by wind.

which requires some assistance from birds and insects for pollination and seed distribution.

Seed dispersal is influenced by a number of factors. Wind and water can carry seeds. Birds and animals eat the fleshy parts of berries and excrete the seed. Some seeds are carried by attaching themselves to birds or animals. Climate can affect the release of seeds. For example the native broom releases its seeds at certain temperatures in summer.

If a seed is dropped or carried to a particular area it will not germinate unless it locates a suitable 'habitat'. A habitat is the particular environment in which a plant or animal, or group of plants or animals, is found living. All living things are best adapted to live in their natural habitat. If they are inadequately adapted they either die or move to another area for which they are better fitted. If change in habitat occurs gradually some plants and animals can gradually adapt themselves to the change and live successfully. Natural habitats vary greatly as do the characteristics of the flora and fauna within the wide variety of natural habitats which occur within the Park.

A natural habitat is shaped by natural forces, and is subject to the continual change which these forces exert. When we look at an existing plant community and its habitat, it is often easy to forget that at earlier stages the same area was the natural habitat of completely different plants and animals.

It is hard to grasp the idea of a place before it had plants growing in it, but volcanic forces in the Park have given us some very dramatic examples of how a habitat may change, and of how various plant communities may succeed one another in a given location. This idea of succession in plant communities is clearly illustrated throughout the Park.

Volcanic activity can disrupt the natural development of plants, but in a short period of time the plant life begins to recover.

Mat plants are especially suited to the rigorous conditions of alpine and desert lands.

47

Over a long period of time a succession of plants will colonise the lava flows. Eventually forests, like this mature beech forest on a lava flow from Mt Ruapehu, will become established.

1800 years ago the Lake Taupo eruption sent waves of pumice sweeping over the Park burying the existing vegetation. The upper layer of this pumice bank still shows the charred logs of once tall native trees.

Consider the lava flows in the Mangatepopo Valley. The most recent significant flows reached the Valley floor in 1954. At first the flow is simply an area of cooling lava, a dry porous rock with no soil, and therefore an environment where trees and shrubs cannot grow.

However, the flow is a suitable habitat for the simple colonising fungi and mosses. As these plants live and die, their decaying remains begin to build up and become the basis for other plants to grow in. As the vegetable matter accumulates it becomes deep enough to retain water and to provide an anchor for larger plants.

Eventually, the accumulation is enough to provide an environment for shrubs. The Te Mari lava flow, which occurred about 800 years ago, is an example of a flow which is now supporting this type of vegetation. Small shrubs provide shelter for the seedlings of large trees. Given a suitable climate, what was once a barren lava flow will over time eventually support a forest.

A good example of this 'final' stage is the beech forest at Ohinepango Springs. Here an old lava flow which covers the base of the spring is now covered with mature beech trees. The idea that various types of plant communities succeed one another in a given area raises the concept that eventually a form of 'climax' vegetation will be reached. This plant community will be well adapted to its habitat and will suppress other forms of community and prevent them from succeeding it.

During the absence of natural events such as changes in climate, or volcanic activity, fire, or depletion of the soil's nutrients, this climax vegetation would continue to occupy the area. However, all of these forces will work together continuously to disrupt the establishment of a static environment.

These changes are often subtle, as in the case of climatic change, or soil depletion, but the Park area can be changed dramatically by volcanic activity.

An example of this occurred about 1800 years ago when the volcanic area that is now Lake Taupo exploded in an eruption that was one of the most massive that has occurred anywhere in the world in recent geological times. Enormous quantities of red hot pumice were shot out from the eruption and spread over a 21,000 square kilometre area from the Bombay Hills in the north to Bulls in the south, even reaching as far as the Manawatu. Altogether, more than 70 cubic kilometres of pumice were expelled in the eruption.

In the Park area, the pumice rolled at high speed like a mighty wave, leaping over hills, pushing a superheated shock wave before it and demolishing in an instant everything in its path. In one cataclysmic event the forest was devastated, and then buried in a blanket of pumice. This ancient forest can still be seen in the form of charred logs lying in pumice layers in cuttings along State Highway 47. Bit by bit nature came back, first lichens, then mosses, now tussock, and eventually the bush will return.

The Taupo pumice eruption is a dramatic example of the special problems that plants have in the Park, for not only do they have to contend with the normal natural difficulties of living with ice and snow, wind and freezing temperatures much of the year round, but they face the ever present likelihood that their natural habitat will be disrupted by the results of volcanic activity.

Other factors have influenced the development of our vegetation. The absence of man or his lack of significant impact until late in our story is an obvious one. Not so obvious is the fact that apart from the moa, New Zealand's forests developed without the influence of browsing animals. Consequently the plants did not develop adaptations to protect themselves against browsing. The thorn bushes and prickly plants of countries in which plants evolved in step with browsing animals are relatively unknown here. Consequently, when the European settlers introduced browsing animals such as deer and opposums, the vegetation was not able to protect itself against them. The botanical time within which such adaptations could develop is so long that, in the absence of control measures, these browsing animals would destroy the native forest as we know it.

Given the existing climate it is possible to describe and define the general limits of various types of vegetation. Two important factors are altitude and latitude. The higher you are (altitude) or the further south you are (latitude) the more likely it is that the climate will be colder, and the more likely it is that there will be great extremes of temperature and rainfall.

There is a risk of assuming that our understanding of weather relates in some way to that of the plants themselves. It is easy to think that the alpine vegetation 'endures' a 'harsh' environment. In fact, the opposite is true. An alpine plant is best suited to survive in

The 1975 ash eruptions from Mt Ngauruhoe covered low lying plants, until Autumn rains washed the ash away.

conditions where there are strong winds, dust storms, snow, frost and extremes of temperature. This is its natural habitat.

On the central volcanic plateau, the Tongariro National Park contains within it a range of altitude from 500 metres to 2,700 metres above sea level. Within this range there are five broad vegetation types. These are, mixed rain forest, beech forest, tussock grasslands, alpine-desert and wetlands. There is much diversity, beauty and interest.

# The climate

Prevailing moist westerly winds strongly influence the climate of the Park. These winds often contain moisture from the Pacific ocean, and as the winds reach the mountain they are forced to rise resulting in a higher rainfall in the west than east. By the time the air mass reaches the crest and flows down the eastern side much of the moisture has been lost.

MOIST AIR

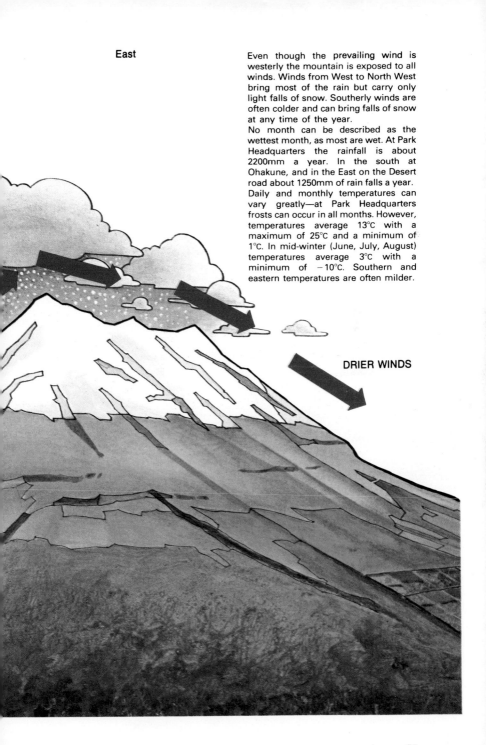

**East**

Even though the prevailing wind is westerly the mountain is exposed to all winds. Winds from West to North West bring most of the rain but carry only light falls of snow. Southerly winds are often colder and can bring falls of snow at any time of the year.

No month can be described as the wettest month, as most are wet. At Park Headquarters the rainfall is about 2200mm a year. In the south at Ohakune, and in the East on the Desert road about 1250mm of rain falls a year.

Daily and monthly temperatures can vary greatly—at Park Headquarters frosts can occur in all months. However, temperatures average 13°C with a maximum of 25°C and a minimum of 1°C. In mid-winter (June, July, August) temperatures average 3°C with a minimum of −10°C. Southern and eastern temperatures are often milder.

**DRIER WINDS**

# Life zones

Many physical and climatic factors determine the range of Tongariro's plant and animal communities. Boundaries between communities are seldom sharply defined but rather merge together in broad zones of transition.

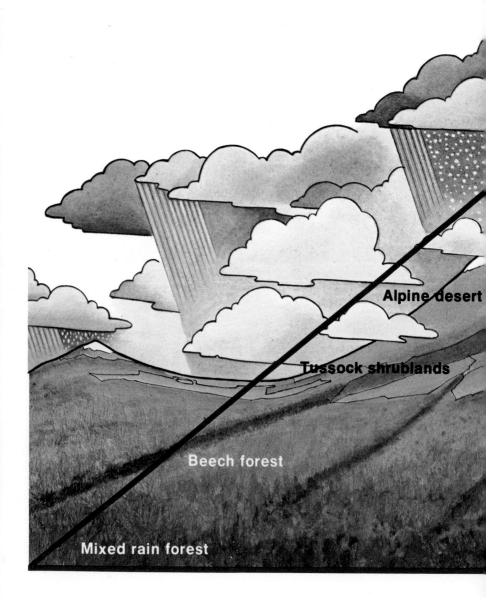

Alpine desert

Tussock shrublands

Beech forest

Mixed rain forest

The higher you go, average daily temperature drops at the rate of about 4°C per 1000 metres. Rainfall, wind strength and evaporation loss increase these factors along with others such as north and south exposure, availability of moisture, seasonal snow cover and volcanic activity which all combine to determine the range of each community.

See page 56

# A mountain profile

This diagram represents the profile of the western slopes of Mount Ruapehu. The life communities are somewhat different from the mountain slopes on the eastern side, mainly because of the difference in annual precipitation.

## Alpine—desert lands

Plants and animals that live in these areas are conditioned to live in an alpine environment; typically the plants are low to the ground, their leaves are adapted to reduce excessive moisture loss.

## Tussock shrublands

These areas form a small but important part of the mountain profile with alpine plants and tussock the dominant species. Snow can cover the vegetation for considerable periods.

## Beech Forest

Mountain beech can be found in the rain forest, but above about the 1000m level they dominate the vegetation. Mountain cedar can be found in this zone also.

## Mixed Rain Forest

These forests found in the lower areas of the Park are rich in diversity. Here, one finds large podocarp trees, climbing vines, broadleafs, ferns and orchids. Here live many of the birds that inhabit the Park.

Tarns and lakes

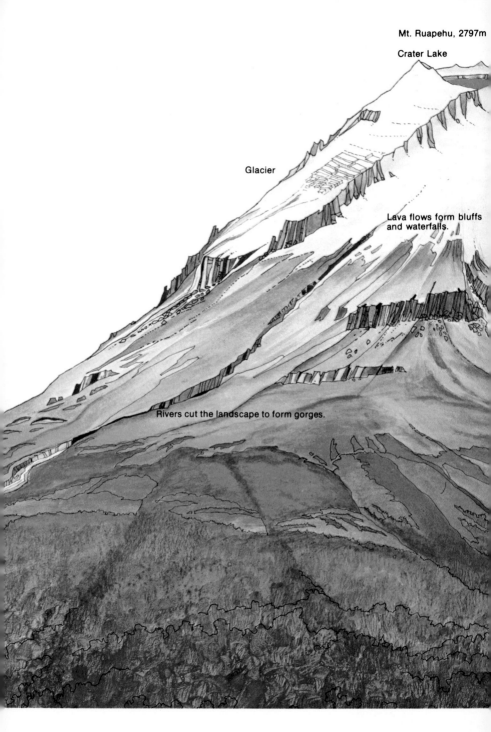

Mt. Ruapehu, 2797m

Crater Lake

Glacier

Lava flows form bluffs and waterfalls.

Rivers cut the landscape to form gorges.

## Animal life

Compared with the richness and diversity of our plant life, visitors often remark on the comparative absence of wildlife. Because of its isolation, New Zealand has only one land mammal—the native bat. It has a wide range of birds, many of them unique to New Zealand. Our bird life had nothing to fear from ground predators, and numbers of our birds have become flightless. We had no rodents until the Maori introduced the native rat about one thousand years ago.

Within the animal kingdom, there is a complex inter-relationship of creatures. This relationship does not appear to produce successive communities as is the case with plants. Rather, it operates to produce a series of balances. These relationships are called chains because each part of the relationship resembles the link of a chain, each one being dependent on the other.

A typical food chain can be found in the beech forest. Moths live on plant material. They are in turn eaten by small birds such as the rifleman, which in turn is a prey of the native falcon. When the falcon dies, its carcass decays and provides nutrients for plant growth.

Because plant growth is at the root of all animal food chains, areas of greater richness or diversity in plant life will support larger pyramids of animal life. Obviously a large number of riflemen may be eaten by one falcon and so on down the chain. Rain forests support large numbers of insects and these diverse communities of insects will support large numbers of insect eating birds and consequently, a larger number of predatory birds. By comparison, the alpine regions which produce fewer fruits and less plants will support comparatively smaller numbers of insects and birds.

A predator from alpine regions will have to cover a larger territory than a forest based predator.

A change in one part of the food chain can have repercussions on all the other parts of the chain. A very good year for beech seeds can increase the population of small birds and of introduced rodents. This in turn produces more prey for introduced ground predators such as stoats, weasels and ferrets. These animals, in

The forest habitats support a diversity of plants, birds and insect life. In beech forests, like those on the western side of Mt Ruapehu, live animals as different as kiwis and stick insects.

their turn, prey on the increased bird population. By introducing birds and other animals, man has contributed to significant imbalances in the natural animal food chains.

Some of the imbalances result from competition for food. Mice and rats compete with birds for insects and, ground dwelling birds and the nests of some native birds are vulnerable to attack from cats, stoats and weasels.

For these reasons our present wildlife is part of a complex chain in which some introduced animals are competing so successfully that they threaten, or have accomplished, the complete extinction of some native species.

The principles that apply to plant ecology also apply to animals. New Zealand's geographic isolation has influenced the kind and variety of species of animals found here and the complex relationships between them clearly illustrate the simple fact that no action can be viewed in isolation.

# The forest community

A forest is organized vertically like an office building or house, with layers corresponding to stories. The **canopy** is the branches and foliage of tall trees that form a roof over the community. Some trees emerge above the canopy to be **emergent** trees, standing above the canopy. Below the canopy are the **understory** trees: young individuals of the canopy species; and small, shade-tolerant trees that will never become part of the canopy. Beneath the understory branches is the **shrub layer,** occupied by knee-high-to-man-high woody plants; beneath that is the herb layer, where most of the ferns, grasses, and smaller woody plants grow. The **forest floor** is the zone of mosses, orchids, mushrooms, creeping plants, and forest litter (leaves, twigs, needles, feathers, bits of bark, animal droppings, etc.). The forest has a "basement" too, interlaced by plant roots, mycelia of fungi, and tunnels of animals, such as worms.

Each layer of the forest has its characteristic animal species, but most forage over more than one level. Some nest in one story and feed in another. The opossum races back and forth from the forest floor to the highest branches. The forest community also has a socio-economic organization. Every animal (and plant) takes up space and consumes a portion of the available nutrients. Each has a place in the community food chain—as, for example, herbivore, carnivore, or scavenger. Each directly or indirectly affects all the other organisms.

**Emergent**

**Canopy**

**Understory**

**Shrub layer**

**Forest floor**

## Mixed rain forest

This is usually called the podocarp-broadleaf forest. The word podocarp refers to the type of seed common to most of the trees found in this rain forest, while the word broadleaf refers to the leafy shrubs and trees of the understory. The podocarp-broadleaf forests have the greatest diversity of plants amongst all of the vegetation types.

Typically they consist of a number of emergent trees such as rimu, miro and matai. These are New Zealand's most sought after native timber species, and very little now remains of this forest type in its unaltered form. Once it covered almost all of the central North Island.

Beneath the emergent trees are a second group of canopy trees. These are typically more suited to tropical or subtropical background. Common amongst these are kamahi and black maire. Lower again are the shrubs, ferns, orchids and fungi which give the rain forest its subtropical luxuriance.

Perching plants, or epiphytes, are characteristic of the rain forest. These are not parasitic plants but grow initially in the vegetable matter which accumulates in crevices or in the forks of the larger trees and eventually develop extensive aerial root systems.

Little now remains of the once vast expanses of Podocarp-broadleaf rain forests that blanketed New Zealand. The richness of its plant communities cannot be matched by those of the exotic forests.

In a podocarp forest the tall trees host a variety of perching plants.

Creepers, similar to those found in tropical forest are also common. The rounded smooth lengths of supplejack contrast with the hooked teeth of the climbing bush lawyer.

Birds are the most obvious of the forest fauna. Look for the native pigeon with its heavy noisy flight. It thrives on the variety of berry fruits and particularly likes the kaka berry. When this fruit is in season the pigeon may eat so much that it cannot fly.

Less obvious are the nectar sipping tui and bellbird and the insect eating and inquisitive robin, fantail and tomtit.

The forest's insect fauna is much less obvious and you must search amongst the rotting logs, litter and debris of the forest floor, or the crevices, bark and leaves of the trees for a glimpse of the tremendous variety of this little known fauna.

Good examples of this rich and varied forest within the Park are found near Ohakune and around the volcanic mountains of Tihia and Pihanga near Turangi.

Birds are an important part of the link in seed distribution. The native pigeon (opposite), coprosma berries (above).

A rich pattern of ground cover plants
exist at the lowest level of the podocarp
forest.
Bracket Fungi
Green Hooded Orchid
Star Fungi
Fern *Blechnum discolour*.

### The beech forest

There are transition forests of almost every type between the pure mixed podocarp-broadleaf forest and pure beech forest. In some places isolated stands of beech are found in predominently podocarp forest, such as those found around Lake Rotopounamu. In other areas such as Mt Pihanga or Tihia, the mountains have altitudinal succession forest, beginning in pure podocarp forest at lower altitudes, and succeeding to mixed podocarp beech. At higher altitudes, this becomes pure beech forest and then merges with sub-alpine scrub.

There are generally no emergent trees in a pure beech forest and there is a very dense canopy formed by mature beech trees. The life cycle of a beech forest is a complex one and often has at lower altitudes little of the dense understory of the podocarp forests.

There are four main species of beech in the Park, although two are most common. These are red beech which is found in the north and south, and mountain beech which is found in the higher altitudes. Another tree common to the beech forest is the kaikawaka, a tree which is quite similar to the northern hemisphere cedar. Beech trees generally prefer poorer soils and grow to a high altitude in the west and south of the Park. At the upper level of tree growth, the growth habit clearly reflects adaptation to climate. Mature trees two hundred years old may only grow to 2 or 3 metres in height, whereas at lower levels the same species will grow 15 or 20 metres in height. The beech forest above Ohakune is amongst the highest forest in New Zealand, possibly due to the fact that forest on the south side of the mountain was sheltered from the devastating Taupo eruptions which occurred 1800 years ago.

Mountain beech forests have a lateral spread from streams and water courses.

The beech forest is the home of the tiny rifleman, one of New Zealand's smallest birds.

Understory trees common to beech forest are various species of coprosma, mountain cabbage trees, three and five finger and ground lilies. Birds common to beech forest are white-heads, silver eye, rifleman, and occasionally parakeet.

The absence of younger beech trees in many beech forests is caused by the closed canopy cutting out so much light that the young beech trees cannot be established. Once the canopy is opened, often by heavy snowfalls or by large numbers of old trees dying at once, young seedlings which have been dormant for long periods are able to grow quickly towards the light. It is expected that the large number of trees dying back in the beech forest around Park Headquarters will eventually be replaced by new growth once the canopy has opened enough. Quite why the older beech trees tend to all die at once is not known, but this process tends to produce large numbers of trees all of the same age in a particular habitat.

## Tussock shrublands

Tussock shrublands dominate the north and western slopes of Tongariro and extend south towards Ruapehu. Here the 'canopy' is mostly red tussock, *Hebe*, *Cassinia* and *Senecio*. Introduced heather is common here also. An early attempt to establish the English game bird, grouse, was accompanied by the introduction of heather. The grouse all died eventually but the heather flourished, and is still spreading. The botanists tell us that the heather will eventually be suppressed by the return of the beech forest, which once extended over much of the land now covered by tussock scrublands.

Tussock grows from a mat base which forms a thick cushion and retains water very well. The soils beneath are volcanic in origin, loose and light. If the vegetation cover is broken then erosion occurs very quickly. Many of the areas now covered by tussock scrublands were once forested by mature trees but the tree cover was destroyed 1800 years ago by the cataclysmic Taupo eruption. The small islands of totara forest which occur on the northern

71

slopes of Tongariro are thought to be isolated patches which somehow survived the eruption. The ribbons of beech forest which wend their way along the stream banks into the tussock shrublands are slowly making their way back into the area, from which they were temporarily expelled by volcanic events. Not all of the areas once forested will revert to that state—thick pumice layers have altered the water table, and now many areas are too wet to support beech forest. The tussock shrublands are the domain of the powerful native falcon who patrols the vast expanse of the rolling tussock land in pursuit of mice, rabbits and smaller birds. Here, too, lives the pipit with his peculiar lark like call and bobbing stance. Fernbirds also live here but they are particularly secretive and although seldom seen, they can often be heard.

The native falcon preys on small birds and animals in the tussock/shrublands.

Volcanic activity has left a mosaic of forest and tussock land.

## The wetlands

The bogs, stream banks, pond edges and seepages of the Park
are another separate habitat, providing an environment for plants
adapted not only to the high altitude, but also to conditions ranging
from permanent saturation to extreme drought. Plants that are
noted for their ability to survive a wide variety of hostile conditions
are absent from these areas, but the ground is never bare. The
mountain beech, remarkable for its ability to survive where other
trees cannot, gives way to specifically adapted plants more able to
cope with the rigours of low temperatures, high altitude and high
moisture content of the soil. On stream sides, banks and marsh
fringes throughout the Park, delicate plants such as the *Ourisia*,
with their beautiful conspicuous white flowers, and the large leaved
yellow flowered buttercup grow in profusion.

The small everlasting daisy is a particularly good example of adaptation to environment, since it will grow just as well in wet places as it will in dry. Each wetland habitat has a particular group of plants, some prefer sites adjacent to swifter flowing water while others prefer the extensive bogs found on the western slopes of Mt Ruapehu, near Mt Hauhangatahi. Here, the soil is acid and peaty and the water has a high concentration of iron compounds that have been dissolved out of the volcanic ash. Oxygen, given off by plant leaves, oxidises this iron compound leaving a rust like brown sludge, or thin iridescent scum floating on the surface of slow moving or stationary water.

The moist ground in these areas supports a thick covering of bog fern, wire rush and sedge. Some plants of the tussock areas are able to grow in these wet-lands, although often in a stunted form. They prefer to grow on thick mats of humus and leaf debris that have raised the ground level marginally above the surrounding water.

Sundews prefer these wet sites; their red leaves carry a sticky secretion to attract and trap feeding insects which are then digested by the plant to supplement its nutrition. In a few streams, the shy blue duck may be found. The blue duck, or whio to the Maori, is found only in high mountain streams and is no longer common through much of New Zealand.

There are many organisms living in the fresh water ponds throughout these wet open tussock lands. Most streams and ponds support populations of fresh water crayfish, and there is a rich aquatic insect fauna.

Particular groups of plants inhabit the various wetland areas of the Park, ranging from river sides to bog areas.

## Alpine-desert lands

Although there are many vegetation types within the desert and alpine lands of the Park, for our purposes, alpine plants are those adapted specifically to survive in areas with partial snow cover for some parts of the year. They do not include all plants above the lowest point of the winter snow level, but include most plants which would normally have snow cover for several weeks of the year.

Typically, these plants are low to the ground to avoid damage from high winds, but often have roots forming where their branches touch the ground to anchor them against high winds and to resist the movement of loose soil particles. Their leaves are specially adapted to reduce excessive moisture loss. In some cases leaves are small or hard, they appear leathery or they have hairs on one or both surfaces. As in the desert plants, the alpine plants usually have very extensive root systems.

With the onset of winter, these plants regulate their activity to compensate for the cold months ahead, but when the snow melts they flower and seed quickly because of the limited growth season.

There are many good examples of these features amongst the alpine flora of Tongariro National Park, and they include the woolly mountain daisy, the mountain snowberry and the whipcord hebe. The alpine regions are at their most magnificent during December and January when the plants begin to flower. Among the predominantly white flowers can be found the mauve or purple orchids.

The bird life is similar to that of the tussock lands. During winter insects are absent and the tracks of the occasional hare or rabbit are the main evidence of animal life. In summer the insect population expands. Cicadas are particularly prominent at the peak of the summer.

Adaptions enable plants to live in the desert like conditions on the eastern side of the Park.

76

The desert lands have a basically similar plant cover to the alpine regions, with a few additional species. One example is the small native broom which grows only a few centimetres high.

In parts, the desert is barren of plants. The area we call the desert is only a rain shadow area and in fact has quite a high rainfall, approximately 150 cm a year. But it is swept by frequent strong, dry winds, blowing from the northwest off Mt Ruapehu. These prevailing winds have dropped most of their moisture, in the form of rain or snow, on the west or windward side of the mountain. Rather than bringing rain to the eastern slopes the winds dry out the moisture available to the plants by drying out the loose, light soil, so causing sandy, desert-like conditions. Melting snow and rain cut channels in the sandy gravel, exposing bare ground and allowing the wind to pick up loose material to carry across the ground and throw at those plants trying to survive.

The small clumps of dead and dying vegetation indicate the struggle that faces plants in this region.

Rocks which trap moisture beneath them are a common focus for plant growth. Stones in this area are frequently covered with reddish brown lichen. There are fewer birds and insects living in these regions as a consequence of the harsh climatic conditions.

Moisture trapped beneath rocks enables plants to survive in harsh desert conditions.

The advancing lodgepole pine, if unchecked will destroy the unique plant communities of these alpine desert lands.

Rainfall can produce flash flooding, and gravel fans and braided streams are characteristic of the Onetapu and Rangipo Deserts. The introduced tree, lodgepole pine, grows here also. This plant has its seed source south of the Park. It was originally planted near Waiouru as wind breaks and later at Karioi as an experiment to assess its suitability for forestry. It proved difficult to contain within its boundaries and it is now no longer used as a forest species. The liberated seeds have been spread north and west to produce an invasion of the Park by this aggressive and tenacious plant.

This tree has been found growing at altitudes of up to 2,000 metres. If no action was taken to prevent its spread it would definitely supress all existing vegetation apart from the forests up to the 2,000 metre level, and this would deprive New Zealand of one of the last remaining vestiges of our unique heritage of unaltered vegetation.

The prevailing westerly wind loses most of its moisture on the western side of the mountains, creating almost desert like conditions on the east. Through this desertscape run the remains of old lahars, glaciers and lava flows.

The pipit lives in the alpine regions and the tussock grassland.

81

# ENJOYING THE PARK

Away in the distant tussock a line of small figures emerges from the late afternoon shadows, moving purposefully towards the comfort and shelter of the hut. The relief of knowing the end is finally in sight means a quickening of step, a hitch at heavy pack straps, thoughts of a hot drink and a comfortable bunk.

Feet that have walked 20 kilometres across Tongariro's heartland are soon resting under the table, while the hubbub of conversation mingles with the clash of the stove door as an arm load of wood tumbles into the fire. They're all talking like old friends to those whom they've just met, remembering a previous night at Rangipo or Waihohonu, or Ketetahi when the wind howled all night or everyone had to double bunk because the hut was bulging at the seams.

Many of us wonder about the sanity of those who walk up and down mountain sides for 6 to 8 hours a day, sleep in overcrowded huts at night, catch a hasty breakfast in the morning before stepping out in their shorts into the frosty air for another 6 or 8 hours of walking. But once you've tried it you appreciate what it's all about and how good it feels to get to the end of the day and know you've enjoyed the Park to the full. It's called tramping.

In Tongariro there are recreational opportunities for everyone.

Who cares about the rain, when you are in a landscape like this—the Oturere Valley.

The Tongariro National Park offers a very wide variety of recreational opportunities, but they all demand of the Park visitor a degree of physical exertion. If you wish to ski, rock or mountain climb, tramp, study the flora and fauna or volcanic activity, it's likely to involve you in walking to where you want to be. But the results will be worth it.

Whatever your chosen recreational activity, we hope that you have an enjoyable time, and ask that you remember that you are within a National Park. The Park only exists because New Zealanders have decided this is an area which should be left as undisturbed as possible. Please be careful with rubbish, and don't injure or remove vegetation. With your co-operation we will attempt to make sure that future generations can enjoy the same special qualities that give us all so much pleasure today.

The three Ranger Stations, at Whakapapa, Turangi and Ohakune, provide information services and advice to supplement that provided in this and the next chapter. Conditions in various parts of the Park can change, and it's wise before setting out on any recreational activity to get up to date information. This should cover not only the weather, but also, if you're tramping, the condition of tracks, huts and fuel supplies. It's advisable, too, to give the Rangers details of your tramping plans, and to fill out the

Throughout the Park there are short walks which can provide a variety of experiences and scenery.

visitors' books in the huts so that if a Ranger needs to know where you are he can easily find you. A good deal of information is contained in the main Park map, NZMS 273, available from Government Bookshops, or the Ranger Stations. Changes can occur between reprints of the map, and if you're in any doubt take your copy to a Ranger Station to check that it is still up to date.

Pamphlets with detailed information on huts and tracks are also available from the Ranger Stations.

Because the Park is situated in a mountainous region, the weather can deteriorate very quickly. For those not properly equipped there is a very real danger from exposure. Even for short walks a parka and woollen jersey are desirable and on longer tramps a full set of equipment is essential.

In winter, snow and ice can make many areas in the Park dangerous for people who lack mountaineering experience or equipment. There can be occasional problems with crevasses and avalanches, particularly at higher altitudes. Storms can make these areas of the Park dangerous in any season and fresh snowfalls have

been recorded even in December and January. If in doubt, ask a Ranger about conditions. In the event of an accident, contact a staff member, Ranger Station or the Police, immediately.

If you're planning a long trip in the Park, leave a note of your intentions with a responsible person who can contact a Ranger Station or the Police if you fail to return on time.

Throughout the Park there are many short family walks, leading to a number of waterfalls, springs, lookout points, picnic and swimming spots as well as other features of interest. Near the Park Headquarters walks available include:

**RIDGE TRACK:** This is a short walk that starts 100 metres uphill from the Park Headquarters. The gently graded track climbs through bush until the shrubland countryside is reached. From here (1189 metres asl) excellent views over the Whakapapa Village to the pastoral lands on the west of the Park can be obtained. Time: 15–20 minutes one way.

**TARANAKI FALLS:** An easy two hour walk with a wide variety of vegetation and geological features, the Taranaki Falls walk begins near Park Headquarters and travels out towards Mt Ngauruhoe, turning a complete circle to return home. Walkers can choose to go from left to right—perhaps the better choice for the first time—or from right to left.

If you take the lower path you walk across tussock/shrubland before stepping into beech forest that fills the valley of the Wairere Stream. The stream is followed up a pleasant gorge until the falls are reached. Here the Wairere pours over the lip of a great lava flow that marches its dark cliffs down the mountain side. The stream has worn its path into the lava, and drops into a pool of boulders.

Above the fall, the clear pattern of the volcanic activity can be seen in the stream banks with their layered ashes from different eruptions. The walk back to the Park Headquarters crosses mainly tussock/shrubland, with small fringes of beech forest in the deep stream valleys.

**SILICA RAPIDS:** The Silica Rapid walk, which leads from the bridge across the Whakapapanui Stream just uphill from the camping ground, across to and alongside the Waikare Stream to the Silica Springs at its source and then back to the Bruce Road, is a comfortable 6 kilometres. To many Park visitors, the highlight of the walk will be the beautiful white rapids just below the springs, but equally attractive are the delicate greenery of the beech forest with its ferns, the riflemen, the golden brown tussock lands or the bog areas.

To begin with the track leads through beech forest, and then across a boglands area, until you are back into beech forest. The Waikare Stream is met and crossed at an impressive rapid where the water has carved its path through solid rock. At the junction with the track to the Whakapapaiti Valley, you turn uphill and follow the Waikare Stream, where you may see a pair of blue ducks. Further uphill, at the attractive Punaruke waterfall there is a natural amphitheatre formed by ancient lava and lahar flows. Shortly after this you leave the beech forest behind, and before long reach the rapids themselves. A little further up the hill are the springs. Then it's a walk across the sub-alpine area back to Bruce Road and down to the village. Time: 3 hours for the round trip.

**WHAKAPAPANUI TRACK:** The Whakapapanui walk follows the Whakapapanui Stream from the Alpine Garden just above the Park Headquarters to the main road about 3 kilometres below the Chateau. The track travels mainly through beech forest and takes about 60 minutes one way.

## LAKE ROTOPOUNAMU

In the Turangi area there are two extremely pleasant walks, both of which can be reached from the Saddle Road between Tongariro and Turangi. The first of these is the track to and around Lake Rotopounamu, a small but very beautiful lake sheltering amongst the podocarp forest on the slopes of Mt Pihanga. The track to the lake is signposted from the roadside on the southern side of the saddle, and there is a pleasant walk of 20 minutes until the lake is reached.

The stillness is broken only by the plop of the scaup, who find this lake an ideal environment, as they search for food amongst the shallows, by the call of the tui or bellbird in the forest, or by the quiet spiral of a leaf falling into the reflecting water. One of the most attractive walks in the Park, it takes one and a half hours to walk right around and back to the road.

If you continue to head north, just after you drop over the saddle you come across Hinemihi's Track, a short 10 minute round trip through rimu and other podocarps to the ancient Maori track used as the principal access way from Turangi to Rotoaira.

## KETETAHI

From State Highway 47 on the northern side of Mt Tongariro a popular track leads up to the Ketetahi Hot Springs. Ample car-parking is provided, and to begin with the track climbs gently through Hall's totara forest and then steeply until the tussocklands are reached. About two and a half hours from the carpark the springs are reached. This thermal area covers many hectares, with fumeroles, boiling mud, blow holes, minor geysers and hot springs all contributing to an exciting spectacle. However, it is unwise to leave the marked track, and if the steam is too heavy, wait until it clears so that you can see where you are.

A bathe in the warm stream below the area is very pleasant, and in earlier days the local Maoris made use of its health giving properties.

A steep sided lava flow and its torrent of melt water provide no obstacle for these young adventurers. The solitude and soft light enhance a late afternoon walk. The silent waters of Lake Rotopounamu are surrounded by tall rain forest.

# MANGAWHERO FOREST

At Ohakune there are a number of pleasant walks which take full advantage of the majestic podocarp, red and silver beech forests. The Mangawhero Forest walk begins outside the Ohakune Ranger Station at the bottom of the Ohakune Mountain Road. If you take the left hand side of the walk the river you cross is the Mangawhero (the stream of reddish rocks). This river begins in a small gully 1100 metres higher up Mount Ruapehu. It descends over two giant sized waterfalls, carves its way through lahar-deposited material and follows a fault line down the mountain to pass under the bridge, eventually joining the Whangaehu River which meets the ocean south of Wanganui.

From the river the track leads you away from the mountain beech and kamahi dominant canopy in to a gloomy forest with giant rimu trees pushing their way 30 metres or more above the forest floor.

As you approach the sunken volcanic crater you will become aware of the large open area bounded behind by a hill, which is the remnant of a block of uplifted limestone. Water still lies close to the surface of the vent, and supports a swamp type forest. The buttressed kahikatea, the tallest tree in New Zealand, will tolerate continually wet feet, while its close relative the rimu grows in drier places to the edge of this sunken crater. A similar extinct vent a short distance to the west supports a bouncy carpet of spagnum moss.

The track now meanders in and out of gullies eventually descending to the base of the limestone outcrop. This large impressive whitish cliff is tertiary limestone around 3 million years old. Preserved in this block of limestone known locally as Rongokaupo Hill, are complete scallop, oyster and barnacle shells.

The river becomes noisier, the track follows it closely from now on, eventually breaking out into the Mangawhero picnic area. The Mangawhero is crossed again, the track crosses the Ohakune Mountain Road and returns down through fern filled bush to the Ranger Station.

In places along the track rotting pieces of wood cross at right angles. These tell a story of the trams that used to run down through the bush bringing the logs out to the mills at Ohakune Junction.
Time: 70 minutes for the round trip.

## WAITONGA FALLS

A completely different type of vegetation is experienced in the walk to the Waitonga Falls. The start of this track is 10 kilometres up the Ohakune Mountain Road, and car parking facilities are provided. The track leads up, at times a little steeper than a gentle gradient, through beech forest which progressively becomes more stunted as the sub-alpine altitudes are reached.

Then you break into a clearing, with the peak of Mt Ruapehu and Girdlestone Peak as a backdrop to a boardwalk across the boggy wetlands, with its sub-alpine plants. Once across the clearing the track descends into a valley and shortly the impressive Waitonga Falls, at 63 metres the highest in the Park, is reached. Time: Two hours return trip.

## AROUND THE MOUNTAIN TRACK

As well as these shorter walks, the Park offers a network of tramping tracks with overnight accommodation being provided in Park huts located at strategic points, about one day's tramping from each other. From the Park Headquarters, tracks lead north to the Mangatepopo Hut, and east across the tussock land between Ruapehu and Ngauruhoe to either the Oturere or Waihohonu Huts.

Access to the Mangatepopo Hut can also be gained from a spur road leading from State Highway 47. From the Hut the track leads up to a saddle between Tongariro and Ngauruhoe, across the large South Crater of Tongariro to the still active Red Crater and its adjacent Emerald Lakes, small green lakes nestled in old explosion craters. Once past the Red Crater the track divides, one route leading further north to the Ketetahi Hut near the Ketetahi Springs, and the other turning east to the Oturere Hut.

From Oturere, the track passes the Waihohonu Hut, and then begins the long trek across the Rangipo Desert until it reaches the Rangipo Hut beneath the Eastern flank of Mt Ruapehu. The next hut is the Mangaehuehu and some kilometres further on a spur track is reached which leads to the Blyth Hut and eventually the Turoa Ski Field. From the fork it is about a one hour tramp until the Ohakune Mountain Road is reached.

Further up the road, the track starts again and leads west to the Wanganui Tramping Club Hut, and from here across the sub-alpine tussock land to the west of Ruapehu until yet another fork is reached. Here one arm of the track crosses the head of the Whakapapaiti Valley with its impressive water falls bounding off eroded lava flows, and on to the Bruce Road; while the other wends its way down the valley, past the Whakapapaiti Hut and arriving back at Park Headquarters. All together it is a five or six day tramp around the three mountains.

As well as these tracks, which are all well graded and marked, there are a number of others throughout the Park. Full details of all the tracks in the Park, hut costs, camping conditions and difficulty of the walks can be obtained from the Ranger Stations.

Within the Park boundaries certain areas have been set aside as wilderness areas, and remain undeveloped except for a minimum of tracking. The two major wilderness areas in the Park are the Hauhangatahi (8500 hectares) from the western slopes of Mt Ruapehu to Erua on State Highway 4, and the Te Tatau-Pounamu to the north east of Mt Tongariro, between Central Crater and the Desert Road.

The wide range of tracks within the Park offer tramps which can last in duration from a few hours to 5 or 6 days, and from a gentle trek across tussock lands to crossing the summits of the three mountains. If the route you decide to take involves leaving marked tracks you should be able to use your map expertly and be skilled in navigating by compass, as 'white out' conditions do occur from time to time.

The top of Tongariro is a torn landscape of lakes and lava flows.

When you are tramping, we hope you will follow the Nature Conservation Council's Minimum Impact Guide.

## NATURE CONSERVATION COUNCIL
## MINIMUM IMPACT GUIDE

1. Keep parties small—crowds and solitude are incompatible.
2. Plan your trip to minimise rubbish—avoid bottles and cans.
3. Pack out what you pack in—carry out all unburnable rubbish. Burying is unsatisfactory because rubbish can be exposed by animals or frost action.
4. Keep to tracks where they exist—avoid trampling the surrounding areas.
5. Minimise campsite construction—do not damage the vegetation.
6. Avoid camping near huts, roads, open water, tracks and other campers—respect their privacy.
7. Do not use soap or detergents in streams or lakes. Carry washing water to your campsite and drain it into absorbent soil.
8. Bury toilet wastes—select a suitable screened spot well away from water and potential campsites, dig a shallow hole within the 'biological decomposer' layer of the soil. Refill the hole with humus or loose soil.
9. Use portable stoves rather than fires—dead wood is an important part of nature's cycle and is scarce in many areas.
10. If you must use a wood fire keep it small to conserve wood. Before leaving dismantle your fireplace.
11. Protect native wildlife and plants—do not take domestic animals into National Parks. Care for nature's rhythm and balance; you are part of it.

## Skiing

In the winter of 1913 William Mead and Bernard Drake set out in a buggy from Waiouru for the Waihohonu Hut. Armed with skis imported from Switzerland and the only textbook then written in English on skiing, they were about to be the pioneers of a sport that has now grown to be the most popular winter recreation in the Park, and one growing in importance throughout the country.

It was a half day's ride to the hut, and after an afternoon's practice the two were ready for the real thing. From the hut they skied across country to the slopes around the Tama Lakes and the base of Mt Ngauruhoe, and then skied back to the hut. The next day they took two days provisions and set out to see what the Whakapapa slopes were like. "We went up to about 7,500 ft altitude, and were satisfied that this Whakapapa area was much better than any other on Ruapehu for skiing as well as for summer parties, if it could be given road access and huts." Before leaving their hut for Waiouru, Meads and Drake left a note informing visitors that they were organising the Ruapehu Ski Club.

The first hut for the Ruapehu Ski Club was provided by the Tourist Department and taken by bullock to a site William Mead chose at the head of the Mangatepopo Valley in 1918. In 1920 a two roomed hut was built at the end of a newly formed cart track at Whakapapa, at the present site of the Chateau.

Since these early pioneer days the sport has become increasingly popular, with two well equipped ski fields on Ruapehu's slopes now offering skiing to international standards. At Whakapapa the facilities that now exist reflect a true New Zealand spirit. Most of the lodges on the mountain side have been built by the ski club members themselves. And it was the enthusiasm of the club members that led to the formation of a company to operate ski tows. Since then they have been replaced by a series of modern chairlifts, Poma lifts and T-bar lifts, with rope tows for beginners.

Winter brings a change of recreational activities to Tongariro National Park.

These lifts extend high on Ruapehu's western and southern slopes, so that often it is possible to ski until late spring and early summer. Ruapehu is a late season mountain, with skiable snow from late June through until November. Conditions can be good at any time of the season but greater snow depths and fairer weather, make Ruapehu a fine place for spring skiing.

On the southern slopes of the mountain, above Ohakune, a new skifield has been developed at Turoa. Here, lifts provide access to wide open slopes, with the southern aspect, the snow is often drier and the temperatures colder than Whakapapa.

Both fields have recognised ski schools, cafeteria facilities and a public shelter. Ski equipment can be hired on the field at Whakapapa and at Ohakune for Turoa. Up to 9,000 people visit the skifields on a peak day during the season. There are a variety of ski trails and beginners areas are usually groomed.

On Ruapehu's eastern flank there is four wheel drive access to the limited facilities at Tukino Skifield. There are two rope tows and limited club accommodation for people who seek the self-help atmosphere of Tukino's low-key development.

There are ski patrols at each skifield. At Whakapapa the Visitor Safety Services are managed by the National Park Rangers with assistance from volunteer ski patrollers. At Turoa the Concessionaire provides a professional patrol and at Tukino this service is provided by club members. In addition to ski patrol, skifield hazard assessment and snow hazard forecasting and control, The National Park also operates an ambulance service at Whakapapa. If necessary the Park can call on the support of the Police for assistance with Search and Rescue and other emergency operations.

Anyone can learn to ski, but go about it the right way. Like anyone else using the Park, skiers are advised to be prepared for sudden weather changes. Your local ski club or ski equipment supplier will advise you on suitable equipment and clothing. Lessons from a recognised ski school will not only teach you how to ski, but also help you ski within your own ability. Don't over-extend yourself for the sake of exhilaration of speed without control. Stay away from areas marked as hazardous, and follow the advice of those who know the peculiarities of the mountain.

If you have ever wondered why thousands of people flock to the Park each winter's weekend to spend as much time as humanly possible getting cold and wet on the Ruapehu ski fields and still come up smiling, try skiing. You'll love it!

Up to 9000 skiers visit Ruapehu's skifields on a fine winters day.

There are a wide range of opportunities for recreational skiers. The Summit Plateau of Mt Ruapehu.

## Climbing

While tramping and skiing are the two main recreational activities undertaken in the Park, it offers opportunities for many other types of recreation.

All three mountains offer good mountain climbing. Admittedly climbs are short and cannot be compared to those of the Southern Alps. But for climbers many interesting peaks, walls, towers, buttresses and couloirs exist. Hard frozen snow and ice-encrusted rocks are to be expected on all exposed ridges. As a training ground the area is first class, with a wide variety of climbs in miniature form.

Mt Ngauruhoe is probably the most compelling climb. From the Mangatepopo Hut the base of the mountain is less than one kilometre away, and several routes are possible up to the summit of the mountain. In winter the route from the Mangatepopo saddle is probably the easiest. In summer the climb is not a difficult one, although loose stones falling from the upper slopes are a constant threat, and a watch should be kept on the mountain's volcanic activity.

In winter the mountain may be icy, and should be regarded as a climb suitable only for competent mountain climbers equipped with ice axes, ropes and crampons. Under easy firm snow conditions the climb is a sheer delight and excellent for those seeking climbing practice.

On Ruapehu there are a number of favourite routes. Perhaps the most popular is the climb to the Crater Lake. From the New Zealand Alpine Hut at the top of the Waterfall Chairlift at Whakapapa, the route runs up the gulley between Restful Ridge and Knoll Ridge and on to the Whakapapanui Glacier. From the Glacier Shelter (2660 m asl) near the head of the glacier the route traverses west to the Whakapapaiti Glacier, and then uphill to the Col. The Crater Lake lies ahead of you, but an ascent of the ridge to the Dome on your left provides a rewarding view.

The highest peak of Ruapehu—Tahurangi at 2797 metres—has several routes leading to the summit. Ohakune ridge, which runs north from the slopes above Blyth Hut, gives direct access to the summit from the south, while from the crater area an easy route lies to the west of the peak and then up the summit ridge.

Other peaks which are frequently climbed are Paretetaitonga, Te Heuheu, Girdlestone, and the Pinnacles to the east of the Whakapapa ski fields proper. Some of these climbs provide testing conditions which should be tackled only by the most experienced climbers, others are pleasant easy climbs ideal for the beginner.

Again, if you're considering climbing in the area, check with someone with local experience before you set out to make sure you are properly equipped. Carry plenty of food and warm clothing and don't underestimate the chances of the weather closing in. Travel with a reasonable number of other people, a good party size is four people. For those who are just starting out it's a good idea to join a mountain climbing club.

Another type of climbing that is becoming very popular is rock climbing. A limited amount of rock climbing is available in the Park. The rock is generally not good, but one or two areas are suitable. In particular, the lava bluffs on the northern side of Pukekaikiore can provide some challenging rock climbing. The routes are short, and sometimes difficult. If you would like to practise rock climbing in the Park ask at a Ranger Station for more information.

Volcanic landforms have created a variety of challenging climbing opportunities.

# HUNTING AND FISHING

Deer and pigs are found in the Park area, and the Park follows a policy of reducing their numbers as much as possible. At present recreational hunters appear to be keeping at least the deer numbers in check, and possibly reducing them somewhat.

If you're a hunter, you must apply to a Ranger Station for a permit. Although restrictions are kept to a minimum, because of the other uses of the Park some are inevitable. The main ones are that hunting is not permitted—over the Easter weekend; within one kilometre of Lake Rotopounamu; and that dogs are not permitted in the park. Small bore, rim fire rifles, or shotguns are completely prohibited in the Park.

As is usually the case, the best hunting is found in areas that are less affected by other activities. Areas that are worth exploring are the valley systems on the western side of Mt Ruapehu.

Although the Park is close to one of the best trout fishing rivers in New Zealand, or indeed the world, the Tongariro River, trout are not abundant in the Park's rivers. W. P. Mead tells of catching an eight pound trout near the Haunted Whare in Christmas 1913, but these days that would be very much the exception rather than the rule.

However, several of the rivers in the Park are worth trying if you're a keen fisherman, particularly the Mangawhero, the Whakapapanui, and the upper tributaries of the Wanganui. Other fishing areas within easy access from the Park include Lakes Taupo, Rotoaira and Otamangakau.

Licences are available at most sports stores in the district and from Park Headquarters. Further information can be obtained from the Wildlife Division of the Department of Internal Affairs at Turangi.

High on the northern slopes of Tongariro, Ketetahi Hut overlooks Lake Rotoaira.

## Huts and services

The Tongariro National Park is a popular place—each year it attracts over half a million visitors. All the normal services are provided to meet the needs of visitors, but because the Park has a policy of minimising man's impact on the area, some of them are located outside the Park's boundaries.

Within the Park itself, most of the development is centred on the Whakapapa Village. Before any new development proposals are approved, full account of the environmental impact is assessed.

Within the Park, public accommodation is restricted to the Whakapapa Village. The lodges on the ski field are for the use of the members of the individual clubs and their guests only. At Whakapapa, accommodation is available at the THC Chateau Tongariro, which is a high standard tourist hotel, at the Skotel behind the Chateau, which is a motel, and at the Whakapapa Motor Camp. The Motor Camp has cabins, caravan bays, and tent sites and is located in an attractive setting in beech forest. The central amenties block has full cooking facilities, hot and cold showers and a drying room.

The Mahuia camping ground is located in a picturesque steamside setting 6 kilometres from National Park on State Highway 47. There are tent sites and fireplaces for campers but no charge is made.

## Mountain Huts

| | |
|---|---|
| Mangaehuehu Hut | Located 3 km east of Mangaehuehu Stream accommodates 23 in three rooms. |
| Mangatepopo Hut | On the western side of Mt Ngauruhoe accommodates 24 in three rooms. |
| Oturere Hut | Located below Oturere Crater accommodates 23 in three rooms. |
| Rangipo Hut | Located on the poled route, south of the Tukino Road, accommodates 24 in three rooms. |
| Waihohonu Hut | Located near the old Waihohonu Hut accommodates 22 in three rooms. |
| Whakapapaiti Hut | Located in the Whakapapaiti Valley accommodates 22 in three rooms. |

| | |
|---|---|
| Blyth Hut | This hut on the southern slopes of Mt Ruapehu is two hours from Waitonga Falls carpark on the Ohakune Mt Road. Accommodates 22. |
| Ketetahi Hut | A half hour tramp above the springs, accommodates up to 22 people. |

A charge is made for the use of all mountain huts. Enquiries about use of huts should be made to the Chief Ranger, Park Headquarters, Mt Ruapehu; the Senior Ranger, Ohakune Ranger Station, P.O. Box 1, Ohakune Junction; or the Senior Ranger, Box 237, Turangi.

There are a number of huts belonging to the various skiing, tramping and climbing clubs located at Iwikau, Whakapapa and Tukino. A full list of the clubs and contact addresses can be obtained from the Park.

These huts typically accommodate between 12 and 35 people each, with an average of around 26 bunks per hut. Accommodation is restricted to club members and their guests.

Accommodation can also be found in Ohakune, National Park and Turangi.

A number of other services are available in the Park. At Whakapapa the Chateau provides meals for casual guests either in its main dining room or the separate bistro-type restaurant. Snacks are provided at the Tavern across the road. The camping ground has a small general store which stocks essential items and foodstuffs.

On both the Whakapapa and Turoa ski fields skiers may purchase snack type lunches from concessions operated by licensed firms. At the Iwikau Village, there is a small souvenir shop and a ski-hire and ski equipment store. Skiing lessons can be organised at either of these ski fields.

The Chateau runs a Post Office, and the garage opposite the hotel offers a full mechanic service as well as supplying petrol, oil and antifreeze.

Ruapehu Transport Limited operates mountain transport to Iwikau Village in both summer and winter. The "goats" leave from Whakapapa Village, and provide a continuous service during peak winter periods. At other times buses can be booked for trips within and around the Park.

For the Turoa ski field, buses and four wheeled drive vehicles provide a transport service from the AHI Information Centre in Ohakune to the top of the Ohakune Mountain Road.

Car parks are provided at both ski fields, although in winter access roads may be impassable for private cars without chains. Check with the Ranger Stations for information on current road conditions.

The Park is bounded by an excellent roading system—State Highways 47 to the north and west, 4 and 49 to the west and south and State Highway 1 to the east. Roads actually entering the Park area are State Highway 48 to Whakapapa and the Bruce Road to the ski fields, the road to the Mangatepopo Hut, a short road to the carpark at the start of the Ketetahi Springs track, the Tukino road to the Tukino Village, and the Ohakune Mountain Road leading to the Turoa Ski Fields.

The Park is within easy driving distance of all North Island centres. From Whakapapa Village it's 354 kilometres to Auckland, 347 kilometres to Wellington, 305 kilometres to New Plymouth and 255 to Napier. And it is only 100 kilometres to Taupo, with its own unique variety of attractions.

## THE PARK IS YOURS

New Zealand is building a strong National Park system with vigorous public support. The need to preserve some of this fast-changing world is a compelling motive to set aside areas which man himself has not grossly changed. Although preservation is the central theme of National Park concepts, these areas are not intended to be sanctuaries in seclusion. National Parks are created to be used and enjoyed by the public, consistent with the preservation of natural features and the protection and well-being of native plants and animals.

The Park Rangers have been appointed to enable the Tongariro National Park to fulfil its functions. They live in the Park and live for it. Don't hesitate to ask them for information. They are eager to make your visit pleasant and interesting.

We have tried in this handbook to give you a broad outline of the history, vegetation and recreational opportunities of the Park. If you want to know more, we hope that you will visit the Park frequently to explore for yourself. In this chapter we've listed some of the technical terms that may interest you, and have a short summary of some of the other books that might be of interest.

## Botanical Names of Major Plants and Trees in the Park

| Regular Name | Scientific Name |
|---|---|
| Anisotome | *Anisotome aromatica* |
| Astelia | *Astelia spp.* |
| Bog fern | *Gleichenia dicarpa* |
| Bog pine | *Dacrydium bidwillii* |
| Bristle tussock | *Notodanthonia setifolia var. setifolia* |
| Broadleaf | *Griselinia littoralis* |
| Broom (Native) | *Carmichaelia orbiculata* |
| Buttercup | *Ranunculus spp.* |
| Coprosmas | *Coprosma spp.* |
| Creeping coprosma | *Coprosma pumila* |
| Creeping mapou | *Myrsine nummularia* |
| Everlasting daisy (wet areas) | *Gnaphalium spp.* |
| Everlasting daisy (high areas) | *Helichrysum bellidioides* |
| Filmy ferns | *Hymenophyllum spp.* |
| Flax—red flowered | *Phormium tenax* |
| Flax—yellow flowered | *Phormium cookianum* |
| Gentian | *Gentiana spp.* |
| Hall's totara | *Podocarpus hallii* |
| Harebell | *Wahlenbergia pygmaea* |
| Heather | *Calluna vulgaris* |
| Hebe | *Hebe spp.* |
| Himalayan honeysuckle | *Leycesteria formosa* |
| Inaka | *Dracophyllum spp.* |
| Kahikatea | *Dacrycarpus dacrydioides* |
| Kaikawaka or mountain cedar | *Libocedrus bidwillii* |
| Kamahi | *Weinmannia racemosa* |
| Kanuka | *Leptospermum ericoides* |
| Lodgepole pine | *Pinus contorta* |
| Manuka | *Leptospermum scoparium* |
| Maire | *Nestegis cunninghamii* |
| Matai | *Podocarpus spicatus* |

| | |
|---|---|
| Miro | *Podocarpus ferrugineus* |
| Mountain beech | *Nothofagus solandri var. cliffortioides* |
| Mountain cutty grass | *Gahnia procera* |
| Mountain daisies | *Celmisia spp.* |
| Mountain fivefinger | *Pseudopanax colensoi* |
| Mountain inaka | *Dracophyllum recurvum* |
| Mountain toatoa | *Phyllocladus alpinus* |
| Olearia or tree daisies | *Olearia spp.* |
| Orchids | *Thelymitra spp.* |
| Ourisia | *Ourisia spp.* |
| Parahebes | *Parahebe spp.* |
| Pimelea | *Pimelea spp.* |
| Prince of Wales' feathers fern | *Leptopteris superba* |
| Prickly mingimingi | *Cyathodes juniperina* |
| Pygmy pine | *Dacrydium laxifolium* |
| Red beech | *Nothofagus fusca* |
| Red tussock | *Chionochloa rubra* |
| Rimu | *Dacrydium cupressinum* |
| Sedge | *Carex sp. Scirpus spp. Uncinia spp.* |
| Silver beech | *Nothofagus menziesii* |
| Silver pine | *Dacrydium colensoi* |
| Snowberry | *Gaultheria spp.* |
| Snow totara | *Podocarpus nivalis* |
| Sundew | *Drosera spp.* |
| Totara | *Podocarpus totara* |
| Tree daisy | *Olearia arborescens* |
| Umbrella fern | *Gleichenia cunninghammii* |
| Whipcord hebe | *Hebe tetragona* |
| Wire rush | *Empodisma minus* |
| Woolly mountain daisy | *Celmisia incana* |

## Geological Terms

| | |
|---|---|
| aa | A Hawaiian word for the rough jagged scoria lava flows which result from the top surface cooling and hardening while the interior of the flow is still moving. |
| andesite | A volcanic rock of intermediate grade between basalt and rhyolite. |
| dyke | A vertical slab of lava which has intruded into crevices in the parent rock then cooled into a hard rock structure from which the softer parent rock has eroded away, e.g. Mead's Wall. |
| fire fountaining lava fountaining | The eruption of molten glowing lava from a volcanic vent producing an effect like a fountain of fire. |

| | |
|---|---|
| fissure (volcanic) | An extensive crack or fracture in the parent rock from which eruptions occur. |
| fumarole | A steam or gas vent such as those of Ketetahi. |
| graben | A block of land which has faulted downwards (subsided) relative to the land on either side. The Taupo Rift Valley is a graben, as is also the small downfaulted valley of Lake Rotopounamu. |
| greywacke | Grey, hard, coarse-grained sedimentary rocks of Cenozoic or even Paleozoic age, such as found in the Kaimanawas. |
| lahar | A mudflow of volcanic debris initiated by overflow or eruption of a crater lake or by the sudden melting of ice or snow by hot erupted material. |
| lava | Molten rock which issues from a volcano or volcanic fissure; also the same material which has solidified by cooling. |
| magma | The molten rock beneath the crust of the earth which solidifies to form igneous rocks, either within the crust as plutons or extruded from the crust as lava. |
| massif | A block of mountains forming a single connected unit, extensive. |
| moraine | Ridge or mound of rubble deposited at the fartherst extent of a retreating glacier. |
| neve | Compacting snow/ice which later forms glacier ice; the accumulation area of that ice. |
| nuee ardente | A "glowing cloud" of hot gasses and suspended pyroclastic material which is ejected and races down the slopes of a volcano at high speed, incinerating objects in the path; a single such glowing cloud from Mount Pelee wiped out a city and its 30,000 inhabitants in 1902. |
| olivine | An important rock-forming mineral present in the andesites of the Tongariro region. |
| pyroclastic | An adjective describing all volcanic material which has been erupted aerially. |
| ring plain | Gently sloping plain surrounding volcanoes; in the case of Mt Ruapehu formed by lahar debris. |
| rhyolite | Material from an acid type of volcano such as the violent explosion of the Taupo Pumice Eruption; pumice is a type of rhyolite with a very vesicular nature formed by the expanding of hot gasses within the rock, even to the extent that it may float on water when dry. |
| scoria | Volcanic slag, solidified from eruptive material from a basaltic or andesitic volcano. |
| sedimentary | An adjective for rocks formed by the settling of suspended particles from a body of water, as in the Tertiary marine sedimentary rocks formed by the settling of large amounts of slit and mud onto the sea floor where they compacted into rocks when New Zealand was still covered by the sea. |

| strato-volcano | A cone (or group of cones) formed by the successive layering of lava flows and pyroclastic material. A composite cone. |
|---|---|
| subduction zone | The area of remelting of a crustal plate which has turned down beneath another plate. The friction and stress caused by the movement is the cause of volcanic activity above the subduction zone. |
| vent | A volcanic eruptive opening. |

## Scientific and Maori Names of the Birds of the Park

### Forests

| English | Maori | Scientific |
|---|---|---|
| North Island kiwi | Kiwi | *Apteryx australis* |
| New Zealand pigeon | Kereru, Kuku, Kukupa | *Hemiphaga novaeseelandiae* |
| Kaka | Kaka | *Nestor meridionalis* |
| Yellow crowned parakeet | Kakariki | *Cyanoramphus auriceps* |
| Shining cuckoo | Pipiwharauroa | *Chalcites lucidus* |
| Long tailed cuckoo | Koekoea, Kawekawea, Koehoperoa | *Eudynamis taitensis* |
| Morepork | Ruru | *Ninox novaeseelandiae* |
| Rifleman | Titipounamu | *Acanthisitta chloris* |
| Fantail | Piwakawaka | *Rhipidura fuliginosa* |
| Tomtit | Miromiro | *Petroica toitoi* |
| North Island robin | Toutouwai | *Miro australis longipes* |
| Whitehead | Popokatea | *Mohoua albicilla* |
| Grey warbler | Riroriro | *Gerygone igata* |
| Bellbird | Korimako, makomako | *Anthornis melanura* |
| Tui | Tui | *Prosthemadera novaeseelandiae* |

| Silvereye (also known as Waxeye, White-eye) | Tauhou | *Zosterops lateralis* |
| Blackbird | | |
| Chaffinch | | |
| Hedge sparrow | | |

## Open Country

| Pheasant | | *Phasianus colchicus* |
| Banded dotterel | Tuturiwhatu, Pohowera | *Charadrius bicinctus* |
| Skylark | | *Alauda arvensis* |
| Fernbird | Matata | *Bowdleria punctata* |
| Southern black-backed gull | Karoro, Ngairo | *Larus dominicanus* |
| New Zealand pipit | Pihoihoi | *Anthus novaeseelandiae* |
| Redpoll | | *Carduelis flammea* |
| Yellowhammer | | *Emberiza citrinella* |

## Fringe Areas and Residential Areas

| California quail | | *Laphortyx californica* |
| Song thrush | | *Turdus philomelos* |
| Green finch | | *Chloris chloris* |
| Goldfinch | | *Carduelis carduelis* |
| House sparrow | | *Passer domesticus* |
| Starling | | *Sturnus vulgaris* |
| Myna | | *Acridotheres tristic* |
| Magpie | | *Gymnorhina hypoleuca* |

## Rivers, Lakes, Swamps

| Dabchick | Wewia | *Podiceps rufopectus* |
| Black shag | Kawau | *Phalacrocorax carbo* |
| Little shag | Kawaupaka | *Phalacrocorax melanoleucos brevirostris* |
| White-faced heron | | *Ardea novaehollandiae* |
| Black swan | | *Cyngus atratus* |
| Paradise duck | Putangitangi | *Cascara variegata* |
| Grey duck | Parera | *Anas superciliosa* |
| Mallard duck | | *Anas platyrhynchos* |
| Blue duck | Whio | *Hymenolaimus malacorhynchus* |
| Pukeko | Pukeko | *Porphyrio malanotus* |
| Pied stilt | Poaka | *Himantopus leucocephalus* |
| Kingfisher | Kotare | *Halcyon sanctus* |

## All areas

| Harrier hawk | Kahu | *Circus approximans* |
| NZ falcon | Karearea | *Falco novaeseelandiae* |

# Some Maori Place Names

Hauhangatahi      Occasionally covered with snow. An isolated volcanic peak near Erua.

Heuheu      Brushwood or small forest growth, the family name of the donor of the Park. A peak on Ruapehu (formerly North Peak) named in honour of the Te Heuheu family.

Iti      Small.

Ketetahi      One basket. Hot springs on the northern slopes of Tongariro.

Kohatu      Rock. Te Kohatu a prominent rock in the upper Makatote Valley marked the southern boundary of Tuwharetoa country.

Ma or Manga      Stream or branch of a river.

Mahuia      Confluence of streams (or could be stream of the huia). The camp site bearing this name is by the Mangahuia Stream near its junction with the Whakapapaiti. The Mahuia rapids are further north on the Pukeonake Stream. Mahuia is a shortened form of Mangahuia.

Makahikatoa      Stream of the manuka.
This name is given to three streams in the Park—one running east from the base of Tongariro; another draining the south-east slopes of Ruapehu; the third, a branch of the Whakapapanui.

Makatote      Stream of the katote, the tree fern.
A stream draining the western slopes of Ruapehu and spanned by the Makatote railway viaduct.

Makotuku      Stream of the white heron. A stream draining the south-west slopes of Ruapehu and crossing State Highway 4 at Horopito.

Mangaehuehu      Turbid stream, or stream of dashing waters. Glacier and stream on the south side of Ruapehu.

Mangahouhounui      Stream of the houhou (five-finger).
The Mangahouhounui and Mangahouhouiti Streams drain eastwards from Tongariro.

Ngauruhoe      Ngatoro, the Maori priest who when ascending the mountain for the first time sacrificed a slave named Auruhoe as an offering to the Gods.

Nui      Large

Ohinepango      The place of the dark-skinned girl, Hinepango. A spring and stream feeding the Ohinepango Stream which flows into the Waihohonu Stream.

Onetapu      Sacred sand. Alternative name for Rangipo Desert. Maori travellers did not tarry in crossing these sands for fear of angering the mountain gods; nor did they permit the use of the charred wood found there for cooking.

| | |
|---|---|
| Pare-te-tai-tonga | 'Dust (i.e. snow) from the Southern Sea', in allusion to the icecap and to the heavy falls of snow which accompanied southerly gales. |
| Pihanga | A window-like opening in the roof of large houses to let the smoke out. The crater of Mt. Pihanga is thought to resemble such an opening. |
| Piripiri | Bidi-bidi, sp. Te Piripipi Stream drains the eastern slopes of Ruapehu. |
| Puke | Hill. |
| Pukekaikiore | Hill where the human rats were eaten—where the Ngati Tuwharetoa tribe defeated the Ngati Hotu people about 400 years ago. Pukekaikiore is the volcanic cone east of the Mangatepopo Hut. |
| Pukeonake | Even-sloping hill. The volcanic cone west of the Mangatepopo Hut and the name of a stream running west from the cone. |
| Puna | Spring of water. |
| Rangipo | Darkened sky (probably referring to a volcanic eruption). The Onetapu Desert bears this name also. Probably the name, Rangipo, originally applied broadly to the region between the volcanoes and the Kaimanawa Mountains. Restriction of its use to this would save much confusion. |
| Roto | Lake. |
| Ruapehu | The explosive sounding crater. The highest mountain of the Ruapehu-Ngauruhoe-Tongariro trio. |
| Tangiwai | 'Sound of waters' voice of river or waterfall rising and falling like a maori lament. |
| Tawhai | The beech tree. This name is given to the falls on the Whakapapanui Stream and to a branch of the Whakapapaiti crossing State Highway 48 at the Chateau Tongariro turnoff. |
| Tongariro | 'Tonga' (south wind); 'riro' (carried away or seized). |
| Wai | Water. |
| Waihohonu | Deep river. A stream draining the south-east slopes of Ngauruhoe. |
| Waikato | Flowing waters. J. Grace in his book "Tuwharetoa" gives Waikato as meaning "gathered waters" considering it to refer to the backing up of water in the Taupo basin when the basin was formed. The Waikato River runs northwards along the eastern margin of the Park. This is now called the Tongariro River below the mouth of the Waihohonu Stream. |
| Waimarino | Calm waters. A stream rising near Waikune Prison and the former name of National Park township. |
| Whakapapa | To lay out flat. After an inter-tribal battle the bodies of the defeated were laid out here before the feast. The Whakapapa Village is the site of the Chateau Tongariro and the Park Headquarters. The Whakapapa ski field extends from the terminus of |

|                |                                                                                                                                                         |
| -------------- | ------------------------------------------------------------------------------------------------------------------------------------------------------- |
|                | State Highway 48 to the Whakapapa Glacier and is drained by the upper reaches of the Whakapapaiti and the Whakapapanui Streams.                           |
| Whangaehu      | Turbid river. The glacier and sulphurous river draining the eastern slopes of Ruapehu but later flowing west to cross State Highway 49 at Tangiwai.       |

# BIBLIOGRAPHY

**National Parks of New Zealand**
Leonard Cobb, James Duncan, Rigby International 1980

**Tongariro National Park**
G. W. Johnson, Bascands

**The Forest World of New Zealand**
J. H. Johns and C. G. R. Chavesse, Reeds 1975

**The Tongariro Track**
Phillip Temple, Shell Guide 1976

**Memories of a Mountain and a River**
W. P. Mead, Wanganui Printers, 1979

**New Zealand Adrift**
Graeme Stevens, Reeds 1980

**The Birds Around Us**
Geoff Moon, Heinemann 1979

**Bibliography for Tongariro National Park**
L. H. Turnbull, Dept. of Lands & Survey 1979

**Publications Out of Print:**
**Tuwharetoa**—A History of the Maori People of the Taupo District. A. Te H. Grace, A. H. & A. W. Reed, Wellington 1959

**Volcanoes of Tongariro National Park**
D. R. Gregg, DSIR 1961

**The Tongariro National Park**
J. Cowan Published in 1927—well worth reading

**Ruapehu—Tribute to a Mountain**
J. C. Graham, Reeds

## THANKS

Many people have helped in the preparation of this book —providing copy, ideas, photographs and inspiration. Our thanks are due to them all.

In particular, Bruce Jefferies, Chief Ranger at the Park and his fellow rangers, the Ecology and Geological Survey Divisions of the D.S.I.R., the Wildlife Service of the Department of Internal Affairs, the Department of Lands and Survey, and A. G. Bagnall for help with the Historical section deserve special mention.

Editor: Peter Debreceny
Artwork: Design and Publishing Co-ordinator: Leonard Cobb.

### Photographs

Alexander Turnbull Library
Wallace Grey Studios
R. Van de Voort
Department of Lands and Survey
Tongariro National Park

| | |
|---|---|
| D. Bamford | B. Hollick |
| B. Biggs | J. Nankervis |
| P. Braggins | M. Reedy |
| R. Button | J. Scobie |
| L. Cobb | P. Simpson |
| B. Jefferies | H. Spannagel |
| G. Hancock | B. Zahner |

P. D. HASSELBERG, GOVERNMENT PRINTER, WELLINGTON, NEW ZEALAND—1983

89019H—10,000/10/82PTK